MEI STRUCTURED MATHEMATICS

THIRD EDITION

Statistics 2

Michael Davies
Anthony Eccles
Bob Francis
Nigel Green
Roger Porkess

Series Editor: Roger Porkess

Hodder·Murray
A MEMBER OF THE HODDER HEADLINE GROUP

Acknowledgements

We are grateful to the following companies, institutions and individuals who have given permission to reproduce photographs in this book. Every effort has been made to trace and acknowledge ownership of copyright. The publishers will be glad to make suitable arrangements with any copyright holders whom it has not been possible to contact.

Photographs:
Walter Hodges/CORBIS (page 1); bdi-images (page 12); Hodder Picture Library (pages 18, 32 and 68); Columbia Pictures/RGA (page 81 left); Dreamworks SKG/ RGA (page 81 right); Glyn Kirk/Action-Plus Photographic (page 104)

OCR, AQA and Edexcel accept no responsibility whatsoever for the accuracy or method of working in the answers given.

Hodder Headline's policy is to use papers that are natural, renewable and recyclable products and made from wood grown in sustainable forests. The logging and manufacturing processes are expected to conform to the environmental regulations of the country of origin.

Orders: please contact Bookpoint Ltd, 130 Milton Park, Abingdon, Oxon OX14 4SB. Telephone: (44) 01235 827720, Fax: (44) 01235 400454. Lines are open from 9 am to 6 pm, Monday to Saturday, with a 24-hour message-answering service. You can also order from our website at www.hoddereducation.co.uk.

British Library Cataloguing in Publication Data
A catalogue record for this title is available from The British Library.

ISBN-10: 0340 88853 9
ISBN-13: 978 0 340 88853 7

First Edition Published 1993
Second Edition Published 2000
Third Edition Published 2005
Impression number   10 9 8 7 6 5 4 3 2 1
Year   2012 2011 2010 2009 2008 2007 2006 2005

Copyright © 1993, 2000, 2005 Michael Davies, Anthony Eccles, Bob Francis, Nigel Green, Roger Porkess

Typeset by Tech-Set Ltd, Gateshead, Tyne & Wear.
Printed in Great Britain for Hodder Murray, a member of the Hodder Headline Group, 338 Euston Road, London NW1 3BH by Martins the Printers, Berwick-upon-Tweed.

MEI Structured Mathematics

Mathematics is not only a beautiful and exciting subject in its own right but also one that underpins many other branches of learning. It is consequently fundamental to the success of a modern economy.

MEI Structured Mathematics is designed to increase substantially the number of people taking the subject post-GCSE, by making it accessible, interesting and relevant to a wide range of students.

It is a credit accumulation scheme based on 45 hour units which may be taken individually or aggregated to give Advanced Subsidiary (AS) and Advanced GCE (A Level) qualifications in Mathematics and Further Mathematics. The units may also be used to obtain credit towards other types of qualification.

The course is examined by OCR (previously the Oxford and Cambridge Schools Examination Board) with examinations held in January and June each year.

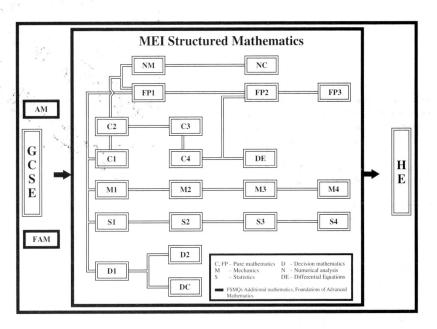

This is one of the series of books written to support the course. Its position within the whole scheme can be seen in the diagram above.

Mathematics in Education and Industry (MEI) is an independent curriculum development body which aims to promote links between education and industry in mathematics. MEI produce relevant examination specifications at GCSE, AS and A Level (including Further Mathematics) and for Free Standing Mathematics Qualifications (FSMQs); these are examined by OCR.

In partnership with Hodder Murray, MEI are responsible for three major series of textbooks: Formula One Maths for Key Stage 3, Hodder Mathematics for GCSE and the MEI Structured Mathematics series, including this book, for AS and A Level.

As well as textbooks, MEI take a leading role in the development of on-line resources to support mathematics. The books in this series are complemented by a major MEI website providing full solutions to the exercises, extra questions including on-line multiple choice tests, interactive demonstrations of the mathematics, schemes of work, and much more.

In recent years MEI have worked hard to promote Further Mathematics and, in conjunction with the DfES, they are now establishing the national network of Further Mathematics Centres.

MEI are committed to supporting the professional development of teachers. In addition to a programme of Continual Professional Development, MEI, in partnership with several universities, co-ordinate the Teaching Advanced Mathematics programme, a course designed to give teachers the skills and confidence to teach A Level mathematics successfully.

Much of the work of MEI is supported by the Gatsby Charitable Foundation.

MEI is a registered charity and a charitable company.

MEI's website and email addresses are www.mei.org.uk and office@mei.org.uk.

Introduction

This is the second in a series of books written to support the Statistics modules in MEI Structured Mathematics, but you may also use them for an independent course in the subject. Throughout the course the emphasis is on understanding, interpretation and modelling, rather than on mere routine calculations. This is the third edition of this book.

There are four chapters in this book. The Poisson distribution is covered in the first chapter and this is followed by the Normal distribution in Chapter 2. Chapter 3 is about samples and hypothesis testing. The book ends with a chapter on bivariate data, covering correlation and regression lines; you meet two correlation coefficients (Pearson's product moment and Spearman's rank) and use them as statistics for suitable hypothesis tests.

Several examples are taken from the pages of a fictional local newspaper, *The Avonford Star*. Much of the information that you receive from the media is of a broadly statistical nature. In these books you are encouraged to recognise this and shown how to evaluate what you are told.

In line with the new specification, in this edition we have adopted the notation S_{xx}, S_{yy} and S_{xy}, with no divisors; thus S_{xy} means $\sum_{i} (x_i - \bar{x})(y_i - \bar{y})$.

The authors of this book would like to thank the many people who have helped in its preparation and particularly those who read the early versions. We would also like to thank the various examination boards who have given permission for their past questions to be included in the exercises. In addition, thanks are due to Bob Francis for his work in preparing the new edition of this book.

Roger Porkess, Series Editor

Key to symbols in this book

? This symbol means that you may want to discuss a point with your teacher. If you are working on your own there are answers in the back of the book. It is important, however, that you have a go at answering the questions before looking up the answers if you are to understand the mathematics fully.

! This is a warning sign. It is used where a common mistake, misunderstanding or tricky point is being described.

This is the ICT icon. It indicates where you should use a graphic calculator or a computer.

e This symbol and a dotted line down the right-hand side of the page indicates material which is beyond the criteria for the unit but which is included for completeness.

☆
☆ Harder questions are indicated with stars. Many of these go beyond the usual examination standard.

Contents

Appendices

Answers

Index

1

The Poisson distribution

If something can go wrong, sooner or later it will go wrong.

Murphy's Law

THE AVONFORD STAR

Website a boost for *Electrics Express*

Business is booming at Avonford's *Electrics Express*, thanks to the emergence of a brand new website that enables customers to buy anything from light bulbs to light fittings, all with next day delivery guaranteed.

Media spokesman, Andy Watts, told *The Star*, 'Since the new website went live, the number of orders for mail order items has increased dramatically. We have taken on more staff to cope with the demand for our products. Orders come in from all over the place. We have found it impossible to predict the pattern of demand, but one thing we do know is that currently we receive an average of 150 orders per hour.

Is there a statistician out there who can help us analyse demand for our products in greater detail?'

The appearance of this article in *The Avonford Star* prompted a statistician from Avonford College to contact *Electrics Express*. She offered to analyse the data and see what suggestions she could come up with.

For her detailed investigation, she considered the distribution of the number of orders per minute. For a random sample of 1000 single-minute intervals during the last month, she collected the following data.

Number of orders per minute	0	1	2	3	4	5	6	7	> 7
Frequency	70	215	265	205	125	75	30	10	5

Summary statistics for this frequency distribution are as follows.

$n = 1000$, $\sum xf = 2525$ and $\sum x^2 f = 8885$

$\Rightarrow \quad \bar{x} = 2.525$ and $s = 1.58$ (to 3 s.f.)

She also noted that

- orders made on the website appear at random and independently of each other
- the average number of orders per minute is about 2.5 which is equivalent to 150 per hour.

She suggested that the appropriate probability distribution to model the number of orders was the Poisson distribution.

The particular Poisson distribution, with an average number of 2.5 orders per minute, is defined as an *infinite* discrete random variable given by

$$P(X = r) = e^{-2.5} \frac{2.5^r}{r!} \qquad \text{for } r = 0, 1, 2, 3, 4, \ldots$$

where

- X represents the random variable 'number of orders per minute'
- e is the mathematical constant $2.718\,281\,828\,459\ldots$
- $e^{-2.5}$ can be found from your calculator as 0.082 (to 3 s.f.)
- $r!$ means r *factorial*, for example $5! = 5 \times 4 \times 3 \times 2 \times 1 = 120$.

Values of the corresponding probability distribution may be tabulated using the formula, together with the *expected* frequencies this would generate. For example

$$P(X = 4) = e^{-2.5} \frac{2.5^4}{4!}$$

$$= 0.133\,60\ldots = 0.134 \text{ (to 3 s.f.)}$$

Number of orders per minute (r)	0	1	2	3	4	5	6	7	> 7
Observed frequency	70	215	265	205	125	75	30	10	5
$P(X = r)$	0.082	0.205	0.257	0.214	0.134	0.067	0.028	0.010	0.003
Expected frequency	82	205	257	214	134	67	28	10	3

The closeness of the observed and expected frequencies (see figure 1.1) implies that the Poisson distribution is indeed a suitable model in this instance.

Note also that the sample mean, $\bar{x} = 2.525$, is very close to the sample variance, $s^2 = 2.509$ (to 4 s.f.). You will see later that, for a Poisson distribution, the expectation and variance are the same. So the closeness of these two summary statistics provides further evidence that the Poisson distribution is a suitable model.

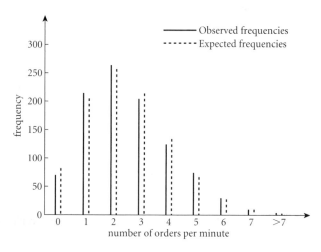

Figure 1.1

The Poisson distribution

A discrete random variable may be modelled by a Poisson distribution provided

- events occur at random and independently of each other, in a given interval of time or space
- the average number events in the given interval, λ, is uniform and finite.

Let X represent the number of occurrences in a given interval, then

$$P(X = r) = e^{-\lambda} \frac{\lambda^r}{r!} \qquad \text{for } r = 0, 1, 2, 3, 4, \ldots$$

Like the discrete random variables you met in *Statistics 1*, the Poisson distribution may be illustrated by a vertical line chart. The shape of the Poisson distribution depends on the value of the parameter λ (pronounced 'lambda'). If λ is small the distribution has positive skew, but as λ increases the distribution becomes progressively more symmetrical. Three typical Poisson distributions are illustrated in figure 1.2.

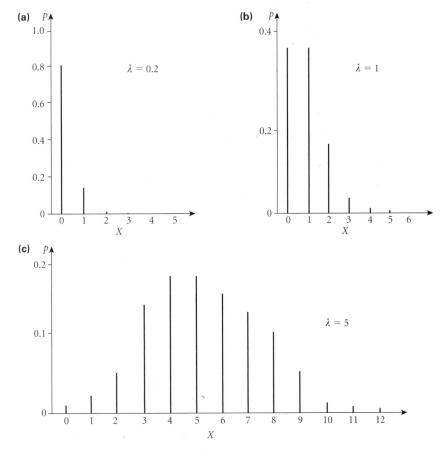

Figure 1.2 The shape of the Poisson distribution for **(a)** $\lambda = 0.2$ **(b)** $\lambda = 1$ **(c)** $\lambda = 5$

There are many situations in which events happen singly and the average number of occurrences per given interval of time or space is uniform and is known or can be easily found. Such events might include: the number of goals scored by a team in a football match, the number of telephone calls received per minute at an exchange, the number of accidents in a factory per week, the number of particles emitted in a minute by a radioactive substance, the number of typing errors per page in a document, the number of flaws per metre in a roll of cloth or the number of micro-organisms in 1 millilitre of pond water.

EXAMPLE 1.1

The number of defects in a wire cable can be modelled by the Poisson distribution with a uniform rate of 1.5 defects per kilometre.

Find the probability that
(i) a single kilometre of wire will have exactly 3 defects
(ii) a single kilometre of wire will have at least 5 defects.

SOLUTION

Let X represent the number of defects per kilometre, then

$$P(X = r) = e^{-1.5} \frac{1.5^r}{r!} \qquad \text{for } r = 0, 1, 2, 3, 4, \ldots .$$

(i) $P(X = 3) = e^{-1.5} \dfrac{1.5^3}{3!}$

$$= 0.125\,510\ldots$$
$$= 0.126 \text{ (to 3 s.f.)}$$

(ii) $P(X \geqslant 5) = 1 - [P(X = 0) + P(X = 1) + P(X = 2) + P(X = 3) + P(X = 4)]$

$$= 1 - \left[e^{-1.5} \frac{1.5^0}{0!} + e^{-1.5} \frac{1.5^1}{1!} + e^{-1.5} \frac{1.5^2}{2!} + e^{-1.5} \frac{1.5^3}{3!} + e^{-1.5} \frac{1.5^4}{4!} \right]$$

$$= 1 - [0.223\,130\ldots + 0.334\,695\ldots + 0.251\,021\ldots + 0.125\,510\ldots$$
$$+ 0.047\,066\ldots]$$

$$= 0.0186 \text{ (to 3 s.f.)}$$

Calculating Poisson distribution probabilities

In Example 1.1, about the defects in a wire cable, you had to work out $P(X \geqslant 5)$. To do this you used $P(X \geqslant 5) = 1 - P(X \leqslant 4)$ which saved you having to work out all the probabilities for five or more occurrences and adding them together. Such calculations can take a long time even though the terms eventually get smaller and smaller, so that after some time you will have gone far enough for the accuracy you require and may stop.

However, Example 1.1 did involve working out and summing five probabilities and so was quite time consuming. Here are two ways of cutting down on the amount of work, and so on the time you take.

Recurrence relations

Recurrence relations allow you to use the term you have obtained to work out the next one. For the Poisson distribution with parameter λ,

$$P(X = 0) = e^{-\lambda} \qquad \text{You must use your calculator to find this term.}$$

$$P(X = 1) = e^{-\lambda}\lambda = \lambda P(X = 0) \qquad \text{Multiply the previous term by } \lambda.$$

$$P(X = 2) = e^{-\lambda}\frac{\lambda^2}{2!} = \frac{\lambda}{2}P(X = 1)$$

Multiply the previous term by $\frac{\lambda}{2}$.

$$P(X = 3) = e^{-\lambda}\frac{\lambda^3}{3!} = \frac{\lambda}{3}P(X = 2)$$

Multiply the previous term by $\frac{\lambda}{3}$.

$$P(X = 4) = e^{-\lambda}\frac{\lambda^4}{4!} = \frac{\lambda}{4}P(X = 3)$$

Multiply the previous term by $\frac{\lambda}{4}$.

In general, you can find $P(X = r)$ by multiplying your previous probability, $P(X = r - 1)$, by $\frac{\lambda}{r}$. You would expect to hold the latest value on your calculator and keep a running total in the memory.

Setting this out on paper with $\lambda = 1.5$ (the figure from Example 1.1) gives these figures.

No. of cases, r	Conversion	$P(X = r)$	Running total, $P(X \leqslant r)$
0		0.223 130...	0.223 130...
1	$\times 1.5$	0.334 695...	0.557 825...
2	$\times \frac{1.5}{2}$	0.251 021...	0.808 846...
3	$\times \frac{1.5}{3}$	0.125 511...	0.934 357...
4	$\times \frac{1.5}{4}$	0.047 067...	0.981 424...

Cumulative Poisson probability tables

You can also find probabilities like $P(X \leqslant 4)$ by using *cumulative Poisson probability tables*. You can see how to do this by looking at the extract from the tables overleaf. For $\lambda = 1.5$ and $x = 4$ this gives you the answer 0.9814.

x \ λ	1.00	1.10	1.20	1.30	1.40	1.50	1.60	1.70	1.80	1.90
0	0.3679	0.3329	0.3012	0.2725	0.2466	0.2231	0.2019	0.1827	0.1653	0.1496
1	0.7358	0.6990	0.6626	0.6268	0.5918	0.5578	0.5249	0.4932	0.4628	0.4337
2	0.9197	0.9004	0.8795	0.8571	0.8335	0.8088	0.7834	0.7572	0.7306	0.7037
3	0.9810	0.9743	0.9662	0.9569	0.9463	0.9344	0.9212	0.9068	0.8913	0.8747
4	0.9963	0.9946	0.9923	0.9893	0.9857	0.9814	0.9763	0.9704	0.9636	0.9559
5	0.9994	0.9990	0.9985	0.9978	0.9968	0.9955	0.9940	0.9920	0.9896	0.9868
6	0.9999	0.9999	0.9997	0.9996	0.9994	0.9991	0.9987	0.9981	0.9974	0.9966
7	1.0000	1.0000	1.0000	0.9999	0.9999	0.9998	0.9997	0.9996	0.9994	0.9992
8	.....	.....	.....	1.000	1.000	1.000	1.000	0.9999	0.9999	0.9998
9	.....	.....	.....	.....	.....	.....	.....	1.0000	1.0000	1.0000

Figure 1.3

If you wanted to find $P(X \geqslant 5)$, you would use

$$P(X \geqslant 5) = 1 - P(X \leqslant 4)$$
$$= 1 - 0.9814$$
$$= 0.0186$$

EXAMPLE 1.2

Jasmit is considering buying a telephone answering machine. He has one for five days' free trial and finds that 22 messages are left on it. Assuming that this is typical of the use it will get if he buys it, find:

(i) the mean number of messages per day
(ii) the probability that on one particular day there will be exactly six messages
(iii) the probability that on one particular day there will be more than six messages.

SOLUTION

(i) Converting the total for five days to the mean for a single day gives

$$\text{daily mean} = \tfrac{22}{5} = 4.4 \text{ messages per day}$$

(ii) Calling X the number of messages per day,

$$P(X = 6) = e^{-4.4}\frac{4.4^6}{6!}$$
$$= 0.124$$

(iii) Using the cumulative Poisson probability tables gives

$$P(X \leqslant 6) = 0.8436$$

and so

$$P(X > 6) = 1 - 0.8436$$
$$= 0.1564$$

Modelling with a Poisson distribution

In the example about *Electrics Express*, the mean and variance of the number of orders placed per minute on the website were given by $\bar{x} = 2.525$ and $s^2 = 2.509$ (to 4 s.f.). The corresponding Poisson parameter, λ, was then taken to be 2.5.

It can be shown that for any Poisson distribution

$$\text{Mean} = \text{E}(X) = \lambda \quad \text{and} \quad \text{Variance} = \text{Var}(X) = \lambda.$$

Formal derivations of the mean and variance of a Poisson distribution are given in Appendix 1.

When modelling data with a Poisson distribution, the closeness of the mean and variance is one indication that the data fits the model well.

When you have collected the data, go through the following steps in order to check whether the data may be modelled by a Poisson distribution.

- Work out the mean and variance and check that they are roughly equal.
- Use the sample mean to work out the Poisson probability distribution and a suitable set of expected frequencies.
- Compare these expected frequencies with your observations.

EXERCISE 1A

1 If $X \sim$ Poisson (1.75), use the Poisson formula to calculate
  (i) $\text{P}(X = 2)$ (ii) $\text{P}(X > 0)$.

2 If $X \sim$ Poisson (4.8), use Poisson tables to find
  (i) $\text{P}(X \leqslant 3)$ (ii) $\text{P}(X = 5)$ (iii) $\text{P}(X > 6)$.

3 If $X \sim$ Poisson (3.1), use the Poisson formula to calculate
  (i) $\text{P}(X = 3)$ (ii) $\text{P}(X < 2)$ (iii) $\text{P}(X \geqslant 2)$.
  Check your answers by using tables.

4 (i) If $X \sim$ Poisson (10), use Poisson tables to find
      (a) $\text{P}(X \leqslant 12)$ (b) $\text{P}(X = 9)$ (c) $\text{P}(X \geqslant 7)$.

  (ii) Two successive values of X are now chosen independently from the distribution. Find the probability that just one of them is at least 7.

5 The number of cars passing a house in a residential road between 10 am and 11 am on a weekday is a random variable, X. Give a condition under which X may be modelled by a Poisson distribution.

Suppose that $X \sim$ P(3.4). Calculate $\text{P}(X \geqslant 4)$.

[Cambridge]

6 The number of night calls to a fire station in a small town can be modelled by a Poisson distribution with mean 4.2 per night. Find the probability that on a particular night there will be three or more calls to the fire station.

State what needs to be assumed about the calls to the fire station in order to justify a Poisson model.

[Cambridge]

7 The number of wombats that are killed on a particular stretch of road in Australia in any one day can be modelled by a Poisson (0.42) random variable.
  (i) Calculate the probability that exactly two wombats are killed on a given day on this stretch of road.
  (ii) Find the probability that exactly four wombats are killed over a 5-day period on this stretch of road.

8 A typesetter makes 1500 mistakes in a book of 500 pages. On how many pages would you expect to find **(i)** 0 **(ii)** 1 **(iii)** 2 **(iv)** 3 or more mistakes? State any assumptions in your workings.

9 In a country the mean number of deaths per year from lightning strike is 2.2.
  (i) Find the probabilities of 0, 1, 2 and more than 2 deaths from lightning strike in any particular year.

In a neighbouring country, it is found that one year in twenty nobody dies from lightning strike.
  (ii) What is the mean number of deaths per year in that country from lightning strike?

10 Fanfold paper for computer printers is made by putting perforations every 30 cm in a continuous roll of paper. A box of fanfold paper contains 2000 sheets. State the length of the continuous rolls from which the box of paper is produced.

The manufacturers claim that faults occur at random and at an average rate of 1 per 240 metres of paper. State an appropriate distribution for the number of faults per box of paper. Find the probability that a box of paper has no faults and also the probability that it has more than 4 faults.

Two copies of a report which runs to 100 sheets per copy are printed on this sort of paper. Find the probability that there are no faults in either copy of the report and also the probability that just one copy is faulty.

[MEI]

11 350 raisins are put into a mixture which is well stirred and made into 100 small buns. Estimate how many of these buns will

(i) be without raisins

(ii) contain five or more raisins.

In a second batch of 100 buns, exactly one has no raisins in it.

(iii) Estimate the total number of raisins in the second mixture.

12 At a busy intersection of roads, accidents requiring the summoning of an ambulance occur with a frequency, on average, of 1.8 per week. These accidents occur randomly, so that it may be assumed that they follow a Poisson distribution.

(i) Calculate the probability that there will not be an accident in a given week.

(ii) Calculate the smallest integer n such that the probability of more than n accidents in a week is less than 0.02.

(iii) Calculate the probability that there will not be an accident in a given fortnight.

(iv) Calculate the largest integer k such that the probability that there will not be an accident in k successive weeks is greater than 0.0001.

[AEB]

13 A ferry takes cars and small vans on a short journey from an island to the mainland. On a representative sample of weekday mornings, the numbers of vehicles, X, on the 8 am sailing were as follows.

| 20 | 24 | 24 | 22 | 23 | | 21 | 20 | 22 | 23 | 22 |
| 21 | 21 | 22 | 21 | 23 | | 22 | 20 | 22 | 20 | 24 |

(i) Show that X does not have a Poisson distribution.

In fact 20 of the vehicles belong to commuters who use that sailing of the ferry every weekday morning. The random variable Y is the number of vehicles other than those 20 who are using the ferry.

(ii) Investigate whether Y may reasonably be modelled by a Poisson distribution.

The ferry can take 25 vehicles on any journey.

(iii) On what proportion of days would you expect at least one vehicle to be unable to travel on this particular sailing of the ferry because there was no room left and so have to wait for the next one?

14 A garage uses a particular spare part at an average rate of five per week. Assuming that usage of this spare part follows a Poisson distribution, find the probability that
   (i) exactly five are used in a particular week
   (ii) at least five are used in a particular week
   (iii) exactly ten are used in a two-week period
   (iv) at least ten are used in a two-week period
   (v) exactly five are used in each of two successive weeks.

If stocks are replenished weekly, determine the number of spare parts which should be in stock at the beginning of each week to ensure that on average the stock will be insufficient on no more than one week in a 52-week year.

15 Small hard particles are found in the molten glass from which glass bottles are made. On average, 15 particles are found per 100 kg of molten glass. If a bottle contains one or more such particles it has to be discarded.

Suppose bottles of mass 1 kg are made. It is required to estimate the percentage of bottles that have to be discarded. Criticise the following 'answer': *Since the material for 100 bottles contains 15 particles, approximately 15% will have to be discarded.*

Making suitable assumptions, which should be stated, develop a correct argument using a Poisson model, and find the percentage of faulty 1 kg bottles to three significant figures.

Show that about 3.7% of bottles of mass 0.25 kg are faulty.

[MEI]

16 Weak spots occur at random in the manufacture of a certain cable at an average rate of 1 per 100 metres. If X represents the number of weak spots in 100 metres of cable, write down the distribution of X.

Lengths of this cable are wound on to drums. Each drum carries 50 metres of cable. Find the probability that a drum will have three or more weak spots.

A contractor buys five such drums. Find the probability that two have just one weak spot each and the other three have none.

[AEB]

17 A manufacturer of rifle ammunition tests a large consignment for accuracy by firing 500 batches, each of 20 rounds, from a fixed rifle at a target. Those rounds that fall outside a marked circle on the target are classified as *misses*. For each batch of 20 rounds the number of misses is counted.

Misses, X	0	1	2	3	4	5	6–20
Frequency	230	189	65	15	0	1	0

(i) Estimate the mean number of misses per batch.

(ii) Use your mean to estimate the probability of a batch producing 0, 1, 2, 3, 4 and 5 misses using the Poisson distribution as a model.

(iii) Use your answers to part (ii) to estimate expected frequencies of 0, 1, 2, 3, 4 and 5 misses per batch in 500 batches and compare your answers with those actually found.

(iv) Do you think the Poisson distribution is a good model for this situation?

18 A firm investigated the number of employees suffering injuries whilst at work. The results recorded below were obtained for a 52-week period.

Number of employees injured in a week	0	1	2	3	4 or more
Number of weeks	31	17	3	1	0

Give reasons why you might expect this distribution to approximate to a Poisson distribution. Evaluate the mean and variance of the data and explain why this gives further evidence in favour of a Poisson distribution.

Using the calculated value of the mean, find the theoretical frequencies of a Poisson distribution for the number of weeks in which 0, 1, 2, 3, 4 or more employees were injured.

19 A count was made of the number of red blood corpuscles in each of the 64 compartments of a haemocytometer with the following results.

Number of corpuscles	2	3	4	5	6	7	8	9	10	11	12	13	14
Frequency	1	5	4	9	10	10	8	6	4	3	2	1	1

Estimate the mean and variance of the number of red blood corpuscles per compartment. Explain how the values you have obtained support the view that those data are a sample from a Poisson population.

Write down an expression for the theoretical frequency with which compartments containing five red blood corpuscles should be found, assuming this to be obtained from a Poisson population with mean 7. Evaluate this frequency to two decimal places. [MEI]

20 The following table gives the number f_r of each of 519 equal time intervals in which r radioactive atoms decayed.

Number of decays, r	0	1	2	3	4	5	6	7	8	$\geqslant 9$
Observed number of intervals, f_r	11	41	73	105	107	82	55	28	9	8

Estimate the mean and variance of r.

Suggest, with justification, a theoretical distribution from which the data could be a random sample. Hence calculate expected values of f_r and comment briefly on the agreement between these and the observed values.

In the experiment each time interval was of length 7.5 seconds. In a further experiment, 1000 time intervals each of length 5 seconds are to be examined. Estimate the number of these intervals within which no atoms will decay.

The sum of two or more Poisson distributions

THE AVONFORD STAR

Pelican crossing a step nearer for Western Way?

A recent traffic survey has revealed the number of vehicles using one of the main thoroughfares, Western Way, has reached levels where crossing the road has become a hazardous matter.

Council spokeswoman, Rachel Carr, told *The Star*, 'The numbers of vehicles travelling in both directions along Western Way has increased during the past year so much that pedestrians are almost taking their lives in their own hands when crossing the road.'

'Even at 3 pm, usually one of the quietest periods of the day, the average number of vehicles travelling into town is 3.5 per minute and the average number of vehicles travelling out of town is 5.7 per minute. A pelican crossing really is a must!'

She thinks that if they can show that there is a greater than 1 in 4 chance of more than 10 vehicles passing per minute, then there is a chance of getting a pelican crossing.

Assuming that the flows of vehicles, into and out of town, can be modelled by independent Poisson distributions, you can model the flow of vehicles in both directions as follows.

Let X represent the number of vehicles travelling into town at 3 pm, then $X \sim$ Poisson (3.5).

Let Y represent the number of vehicles travelling out of town at 3 pm, then $Y \sim$ Poisson (5.7).

Let T represent the number of vehicles travelling in either direction at 3 pm, then $T = X + Y$.

You can find the probability distribution for T as follows.

$$\begin{aligned} P(T = 0) &= P(X = 0) \times P(Y = 0) = 0.0302 \times 0.0033 \\ &= 0.0001 \end{aligned}$$

$$\begin{aligned} P(T = 1) &= P(X = 0) \times P(Y = 1) + P(X = 1) \times P(Y = 0) \\ &= 0.0302 \times 0.0191 + 0.1057 \times 0.0033 \\ &= 0.0009 \end{aligned}$$

$$\begin{aligned} P(T = 2) &= P(X = 0) \times P(Y = 2) + P(X = 1) \times P(Y = 1) \\ &\quad + P(X = 2) \times P(Y = 0) \\ &= 0.0302 \times 0.0544 + 0.1057 \times 0.0191 + 0.1850 \times 0.0033 \\ &= 0.0043 \end{aligned}$$

and so on.

You can see that this process is very time consuming. Fortunately, you can make life a lot easier by using the fact that if X and Y are two independent Poisson random variables, with means λ and μ respectively, then if $T = X + Y$ then T is a Poisson random variable with mean $\lambda + \mu$.

$$X \sim \text{Poisson}(\lambda) \text{ and } Y \sim \text{Poisson}(\mu) \Rightarrow X + Y \sim \text{Poisson}(\lambda + \mu)$$

Using $T \sim$ Poisson (9.2) gives the required probabilities straight away.
Using tables:

$$\begin{aligned} P(T = 0) &= 0.0001 \\ P(T = 1) &= 0.0010 - 0.0001 = 0.0009 \\ P(T = 2) &= 0.0053 - 0.0010 = 0.0043 \end{aligned}$$

and so on.

You can now use the distribution for T to find the probability that the total traffic flow exceeds 10 vehicles per minute.

$$\begin{aligned} P(T > 10) &= 1 - P(T \leqslant 10) \\ &= 1 - 0.6820 \\ &= 0.318 \end{aligned}$$

Since there is a greater than 25% chance of more than 10 vehicles passing per minute, the case for the pelican crossing has been made, based on the Poisson probability models.

EXAMPLE 1.3

A rare disease causes the death, on average, of 3.8 people per year in England, 0.8 in Scotland and 0.5 in Wales. As far as is known the disease strikes at random and cases are independent of one another.

What is the probability of 7 or more deaths from the disease on the British mainland (i.e. England, Scotland and Wales together) in any year?

SOLUTION

Notice first that:

- P(7 or more deaths) $= 1 -$ P(6 or fewer deaths)
- each of the three distributions fulfils the conditions for it to be modelled by the Poisson distribution.

You can therefore add the three distributions together and treat the result as a single Poisson distribution.

The overall mean is given by

$$3.8 \quad + \quad 0.8 \quad + \quad 0.5 \quad = \quad 5.1$$

| England | Scotland | Wales | Total |

giving an overall distribution of Poisson (5.1).

The probability of 6 or fewer deaths is then found from cumulative Poisson probability tables to be 0.7474.

So the probability of 7 or more deaths is given by $1 - 0.7474 = 0.2526$.

Notes

1 You may only add Poisson distributions in this way if they are independent of each other.
2 The proof of the validity of adding Poisson distributions in this way is given in Appendix 2.

EXAMPLE 1.4

On a lonely Highland road in Scotland, cars are observed passing at the rate of 6 per day and lorries at the rate of 2 per day. On the road is an old cattle grid which will soon need repair. The local works department decide that if the probability of more than 15 vehicles per day passing is less than 1% then the repairs to the cattle grid can wait until next spring, otherwise it will have to be repaired before the winter.

When will the cattle grid have to be repaired?

SOLUTION

Let C be the number of cars per day, L be the number of lorries per day and V be the number of vehicles per day.

$$V = L + C$$

Assuming that a car or a lorry passing along the road is a random event and the two are independent

$$C \sim \text{Poisson } (6), \quad L \sim \text{Poisson } (2)$$
$$\text{and so} \quad V \sim \text{Poisson } (6 + 2)$$
$$\Rightarrow V \sim \text{Poisson } (8).$$

From cumulative Poisson probability tables $P(V \leqslant 15) = 0.9918$.

The required probability is $P(V > 15) = 1 - P(V \leqslant 15)$
$$= 1 - 0.9918$$
$$= 0.0082$$

This is just less than 1% and so the repairs are left until spring.

? The modelling of this situation raises a number of questions.

1 Is it true that a car or lorry passing along the road is a random event, or are some of these regular users, like the lorry collecting the milk from the farms along the road? If, say, three of the cars and one lorry are regular daily users, what effect does this have on the calculation?

2 Is it true that every car or lorry travels independently of every other one?

3 There are no figures for bicycles or motorcycles or other vehicles. Why might this be so?

EXERCISE 1B

1 At the hot drinks counter in a cafeteria both tea and coffee are sold. The number of cups of coffee sold per minute may be assumed to be a Poisson variable with mean 1.5 and the number of cups of tea sold per minute may be assumed to be an independent Poisson variable with mean 0.5.
  (i) Calculate the probability that in a given one-minute period exactly one cup of tea and one cup of coffee are sold.
  (ii) Calculate the probability that in a given three-minute period fewer than five drinks altogether are sold.
  (iii) In a given one-minute period exactly three drinks are sold. Calculate the probability that these are all cups of coffee.

[Cambridge]

2 The numbers of lorry drivers and car drivers visiting an all-night transport cafe between 2 am and 3 am on a Sunday morning have independent Poisson distributions with means 5.1 and 3.6 respectively. Find the probabilities that, between 2 am and 3 am on any Sunday,

(i) exactly five lorry drivers visit the cafe

(ii) at least one car driver visits the cafe

(iii) exactly five lorry drivers and exactly two car drivers visit the cafe.

By using the distribution of the *total* number of drivers visiting the cafe, find the probability that exactly seven drivers visit the cafe between 2 am and 3 am on any Sunday. Given that exactly seven drivers visit the cafe between 2 am and 3 am on one Sunday, find the probability that exactly five of them are driving lorries.

[MEI]

3 A petrol station has service areas on both sides of a motorway, one to serve east-bound traffic and the other for west-bound traffic. The number of east-bound vehicles arriving at the station in one minute has a Poisson distribution with mean 0.9, and the number of west-bound vehicles arriving in one minute has a Poisson distribution with mean 1.6, the two distributions being independent.

(i) Find the probability that in a one-minute period

    (a) no vehicles arrive

    (b) more than two vehicles arrive at this petrol station,

    giving your answers correct to three places of decimals.

Given that in a particular one-minute period three vehicles arrive, find

(ii) the probability that they are all from the same direction

(iii) the most likely combination of east-bound and west-bound vehicles.

[Cambridge]

4 Telephone calls reach a departmental administrator independently and at random, internal ones at a mean rate of two in any five-minute period, and external ones at a mean rate of one in any five-minute period.

(i) Find the probability that in a five-minute period, the administrator receives

    (a) exactly three internal calls

    (b) at least two external calls

    (c) at most five calls in total.

(ii) Given that the administrator receives a total of four calls in a five-minute period, find the probability that exactly two were internal calls.

(iii) Find the probability that in any one-minute interval no calls are received.

5 During a weekday, heavy lorries pass a census point P on a village high street independently and at random times. The mean rate for westward travelling lorries is two in any 30-minute period, and for eastward travelling lorries is three in any 30-minute period.

Find the probability
(i) that there will be no lorries passing P in a given ten-minute period
(ii) that at least one lorry from each direction will pass P in a given ten-minute period
(iii) that there will be exactly four lorries passing P in a given 20-minute period.

[O & C]

6 A restaurant kitchen has two food mixers, A and B. The number of times per week that A breaks down has a Poisson distribution with mean 0.4, while independently the number of times that B breaks down in a week has a Poisson distribution with mean 0.1.

Find, to three decimal places, the probability that in the next three weeks
(i) mixer A will not break down at all
(ii) each mixer will break down exactly once
(iii) there will be a total of two breakdowns.

[London]

7 Two random variables, X and Y, have independent Poisson distributions given by $X \sim$ Poisson (1.4) and $Y \sim$ Poisson (3.6) respectively.
(i) Using the distributions of X and Y *only*, calculate
(a) $P(X + Y = 0)$
(b) $P(X + Y = 1)$
(c) $P(X + Y = 2)$.

The random variable T is defined by $T = X + Y$.
(ii) Write down the distribution of T.
(iii) Use your distribution from part (ii) to check your results in part (i).

8 A boy is watching vehicles travelling along a motorway. All the vehicles he sees are either cars or lorries; the numbers of each may be modelled by two independent Poisson distributions. The mean number of cars per minute is 8.3 and the mean number of lorries per minute is 4.7.

(i) For a given period of one minute, find the probability that he sees
(a) exactly seven cars   (b) at least three lorries.
(ii) Calculate the probability that he sees a total of exactly ten vehicles in a given one-minute period.
(iii) Find the probability that he observes fewer than eight vehicles in a given period of 30 seconds.

9 The number of cats rescued by an animal shelter each day may be modelled by a Poisson distribution with parameter 2.5, while the number of dogs rescued each day may be modelled by an independent Poisson distribution with parameter 3.2.

    (i) Calculate the probability that on a randomly chosen day the shelter rescues

        (a) exactly two cats   **(b)** exactly three dogs

        (c) exactly five cats and dogs in total.

    (ii) Given that one day exactly five cats and dogs were rescued, find the conditional probability that exactly two of these animals were cats.

10 The numbers of emissions per minute from two radioactive substances, A and B, are independent and have Poisson distributions with means 2.8 and 3.25 respectively.

Find the probabilities that in a period of one minute there will be

    (i) at least three emissions from substance A

    (ii) one emission from one of the two substances and two emissions from the other substance

    (iii) a total of five emissions.

The Poisson approximation to the binomial distribution

THE AVONFORD STAR

Rare disease blights town
Chemical plant blamed

A rare disease is attacking residents of Avonford. In the last year alone five people have been diagnosed as suffering from it. This is over three times the national average.

The disease (known as *Palfrey's condition*) causes nausea and fatigue. One sufferer, James Louth (32), of Harpers Lane, has been unable to work for the past six months. His wife Muriel (29) said 'I am worried sick, James has lost his job and I am frightened that the children (Mark, 4, and Samantha, 2) will catch it.'

Mrs Louth blames the chemical complex on the industrial estate for the disease. 'There were never any cases before *Avonford Chemicals* arrived.'

Local environmental campaigner Roy James supports Mrs Louth. 'I warned the local council when planning permission was sought that this would mean an increase in this sort of illness. Normally we would expect 1 case in every 40 000 of the population in a year.'

Avonford Chemicals spokesperson, Julia Millward said 'We categorically deny that our

Muriel Louth believes that the local chemical plant could destroy her family's lives

plant is responsible for the disease. Our record on safety is very good. None of our staff has had the disease. In any case five cases in a population of 60 000 can hardly be called significant.'

The expected number of cases is $60\,000 \times \frac{1}{40\,000}$ or 1.5, so 5 does seem rather high. Do you think that the chemical plant is to blame or do you think people are just looking for an excuse to attack it? How do you decide between the two points of view? Is 5 really that large a number of cases anyway?

The situation could be modelled by the binomial distribution. The probability of somebody getting the disease in any year is $\frac{1}{40\,000}$ and so that of not getting it is $1 - \frac{1}{40\,000} = \frac{39\,999}{40\,000}$.

The probability of 5 cases among $60\,000$ people (and so $59\,995$ people not getting the disease) is given by

$$^{60\,000}C_5 \left(\frac{39\,999}{40\,000}\right)^{59\,995} \left(\frac{1}{40\,000}\right)^{5} \approx 0.0141.$$

What you really want to know, however, is not the probability of exactly 5 cases but that of 5 or more cases. If that is very small, then perhaps something unusual did happen in Avonford last year.

You can find the probability of 5 or more cases by finding the probability of up to and including 4 cases, and subtracting it from 1.

The probability of up to and including 4 cases is given by:

$$\left(\frac{39\,999}{40\,000}\right)^{60\,000} \qquad \text{0 cases}$$

$$+ \,^{60\,000}C_1 \left(\frac{39\,999}{40\,000}\right)^{59\,999} \left(\frac{1}{40\,000}\right) \qquad \text{1 case}$$

$$+ \,^{60\,000}C_2 \left(\frac{39\,999}{40\,000}\right)^{59\,998} \left(\frac{1}{40\,000}\right)^{2} \qquad \text{2 cases}$$

$$+ \,^{60\,000}C_3 \left(\frac{39\,999}{40\,000}\right)^{59\,997} \left(\frac{1}{40\,000}\right)^{3} \qquad \text{3 cases}$$

$$+ \,^{60\,000}C_4 \left(\frac{39\,999}{40\,000}\right)^{59\,996} \left(\frac{1}{40\,000}\right)^{4} \qquad \text{4 cases}$$

It is messy but you can evaluate it on your calculator. It comes out to be

$$0.223 + 0.335 + 0.251 + 0.126 + 0.047 = 0.981.$$

(The figures are written to three decimal places but more places were used in the calculation.)

So the probability of 5 or more cases in a year is $1 - 0.981 = 0.019$. It is unlikely but certainly could happen, see figure 1.4 overleaf.

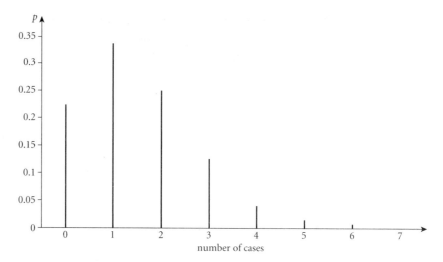

Figure 1.4 Probability distribution $B\left(60000, \frac{1}{40\,000}\right)$

Note

Two other points are worth making. First, the binomial model assumes the trials are independent. If this disease is at all infectious, that certainly would not be the case. Second, there is no evidence at all to link this disease with *Avonford Chemicals*. There are many other possible explanations.

Approximating the binomial terms

Although it was possible to do the calculation using results derived from the binomial distribution, it was distinctly cumbersome. In this section you will see how the calculations can be simplified, a process which turns out to be unexpectedly profitable. The work that follows depends upon the facts that the event is rare but there are many opportunities for it to occur: that is, p is small and n is large.

Start by looking at the first term, the probability of 0 cases of the disease. This is

$$\left(\frac{39\,999}{40\,000}\right)^{60\,000} = k, \text{ a constant.}$$

Now look at the next term, the probability of 1 case of the disease. This is

$$^{60\,000}C_1 \left(\frac{39\,999}{40\,000}\right)^{59\,999} \left(\frac{1}{40\,000}\right)$$

$$= \frac{60\,000 \times \left(\frac{39\,999}{40\,000}\right)^{60\,000} \times \left(\frac{40\,000}{39\,999}\right)}{40\,000}$$

$$= k \times \frac{60\,000}{39\,999} \approx k \times \frac{60\,000}{40\,000} = k \times 1.5.$$

Now look at the next term, the probability of 2 cases of the disease. This is

$$^{60\,000}C_2 \times \left(\frac{39\,999}{40\,000}\right)^{59\,998} \times \left(\frac{1}{40\,000}\right)^2$$

$$= \frac{60\,000 \times 59\,999}{2 \times 1} \times \left(\frac{39\,999}{40\,000}\right)^{60\,000} \times \left(\frac{40\,000}{39\,999}\right)^2 \times \left(\frac{1}{40\,000}\right)^2$$

$$= \frac{k \times 60\,000 \times 59\,999}{2 \times 1 \times 39\,999 \times 39\,999} \approx \frac{k \times 60\,000 \times 60\,000}{2 \times 40\,000 \times 40\,000} = k \times \frac{(1.5)^2}{2}.$$

Proceeding in this way leads to the following probability distribution for the number of cases of the disease.

Number of cases	0	1	2	3	4	...
Probability	k	$k \times 1.5$	$\dfrac{k \times (1.5)^2}{2!}$	$\dfrac{k \times (1.5)^3}{3!}$	$\dfrac{k \times (1.5)^4}{4!}$	...

Since the sum of the probabilities $= 1$,

$$k + k \times 1.5 + k \times \frac{(1.5)^2}{2!} + k \times \frac{(1.5)^3}{3!} + k \times \frac{(1.5)^4}{4!} + \ldots = 1$$

$$k\left[1 + 1.5 + \frac{(1.5)^2}{2!} + \frac{(1.5)^3}{3!} + \frac{(1.5)^4}{4!} + \ldots\right] = 1.$$

The terms in the square brackets form a well known series in pure mathematics, the exponential series e^x.

$$e^x = 1 + x + \frac{x^2}{2!} + \frac{x^3}{3!} + \frac{x^4}{4!} + \ldots$$

Since $k \times e^{1.5} = 1$, $k = e^{-1.5}$.

This gives the probability distribution for the number of cases of the disease as

Number of cases	0	1	2	3	4	...
Probability	$e^{-1.5}$	$e^{-1.5}1.5$	$e^{-1.5}\dfrac{(1.5)^2}{2!}$	$e^{-1.5}\dfrac{(1.5)^3}{3!}$	$e^{-1.5}\dfrac{(1.5)^4}{4!}$	...

and in general for r cases the probability is $e^{-1.5}\dfrac{(1.5)^r}{r!}$.

Accuracy

These expressions are clearly much simpler than those involving binomial coefficients. How accurate are they? The following table compares the results from the two methods, given to six decimal places.

No. of cases	Probability	
	Exact binomial method	Approximate method
0	0.223 126	0.223 130
1	0.334 697	0.334 695
2	0.251 025	0.251 021
3	0.125 512	0.125 511
4	0.047 066	0.047 067

You will see that the agreement is very good; there are no differences until the sixth decimal place.

The Poisson distribution may be used as an approximation to the binomial distribution, $B(n, p)$, when

- n is large
- p is small (and so the event is rare)
- np is not too large (less than or equal to 10).

EXAMPLE 1.5

It is known that nationally one person in a thousand is allergic to a particular chemical used in making a wood preservative. A firm that makes this wood preservative employs 500 people in one of its factories.

(i) What is the probability that more than two people at the factory are allergic to the chemical?
(ii) What assumption are you making?

SOLUTION

(i) Let X be the number of people in a random sample of 500 who are allergic to the chemical.

$$X \sim B(500, 0.001) \qquad n = 500 \quad p = 0.001$$

Since n is large and p is small, the Poisson approximation to the binomial is appropriate.

$$\lambda = np$$
$$= 500 \times 0.001$$
$$= 0.5$$

Consequently $\quad P(X = r) = e^{-\lambda} \dfrac{\lambda^r}{r!}$

$$= e^{-0.5} \dfrac{0.5^r}{r!}$$

$$P(X > 2) = 1 - P(X \leqslant 2)$$
$$= 1 - [P(X = 0) + P(X = 1) + P(X = 2)]$$
$$= 1 - \left[e^{-0.5} + e^{-0.5}0.5 + e^{-0.5} \frac{0.5^2}{2} \right]$$
$$= 1 - [0.6065 + 0.3033 + 0.0758]$$
$$= 1 - 0.9856$$
$$= 0.0144$$

This figure could have been found in cumulative Poisson probability tables.

(ii) The assumption made is that people with the allergy are just as likely to work in the factory as those without the allergy. In practice this seems rather unlikely: you would not stay in a job that made you unhealthy.

1 For each of the following binomial distributions, use the binomial formula to calculate $P(X = 3)$. *In each case* use an appropriate Poisson approximation to find $P(X = 3)$ and calculate the percentage error in using this approximation. Describe what you notice.

(i) $X \sim B(25, 0.2)$ (ii) $X \sim B(250, 0.02)$ (iii) $X \sim B(2500, 0.002)$

2 An automatic machine produces washers, 3% of which are defective according to a severe set of specifications. A sample of 100 washers is drawn at random from the production of this machine. Using a suitable approximating distribution, calculate the probabilities of observing
(i) exactly 3 defectives
(ii) between 2 and 4 defectives inclusive.

3 The number of civil lawsuits filed in state and federal courts on a given day is 500. The probability that any such lawsuit is settled within one week is 0.01. Use the Poisson approximation to find the probability that, of the original 500 lawsuits on a given day, the number that are settled within a week is
(i) exactly seven   (ii) at least five   (iii) at most six.

4 One per cent of the items produced by a certain process are defective. Using the Poisson approximation, determine the probability that in a random sample of 1000 articles
(i) exactly nine are defective   (ii) at most nine are defective.

5 A survey in a town's primary schools has indicated that 5% of the students have severe difficulties with reading. If the primary school students were allocated to the secondary schools at random, estimate the probability that a secondary school with an intake of 200 students will receive
(i) no more than 8 students with severe reading difficulties
(ii) more than 20 students with severe reading difficulties.

6 Betty drives along a 50-mile stretch of motorway 5 days a week 50 weeks a year. She takes no notice of the 70 mph speed limit and, when the traffic allows, travels between 95 and 105 mph. From time to time she is caught by the police and fined but she estimates the probability of this happening on any day is $\frac{1}{300}$. If she gets caught three times within three years she will be disqualified from driving. Use Betty's estimates of probability to answer the following questions.

(i) What is the probability of her being caught exactly once in any year?

(ii) What is the probability of her being caught less than three times in three years?

(iii) What is the probability of her being caught exactly three times in three years?

Betty is in fact caught one day and decides to be somewhat cautious, reducing her normal speed to between 85 and 95 mph. She believes this will reduce the probability of her being caught to $\frac{1}{500}$.

(iv) What is the probability that she is caught less than twice in the next three years?

7 Motorists in a particular part of the Highlands of Scotland have a choice between a direct route and a one-way scenic detour. It is known that on average one in forty of the cars on the road will take the scenic detour. The road engineer wishes to do some repairs on the scenic detour. He chooses a time when he expects 100 cars an hour to pass along the road.

Find the probability that, in any one hour,

(i) no cars   **(ii)** at most 4 cars

will turn on to the scenic detour.

(iii) Between 10.30 am and 11.00 am it will be necessary to block the road completely. What is the probability that no car will be delayed?

8 A sociologist claims that only 3% of all suitably qualified students from inner city schools go on to university. Use his claim and the Poisson approximation to the bionomial distribution to estimate the probability that in a randomly chosen group of 200 such students

(i) exactly five go to university

(ii) more than five go to university.

(iii) If there is at most a 5% chance that more than n of the 200 students go to university, find the lowest possible value of n.

Another group of 100 students is also chosen. Find the probability that

(iv) exactly five of each group go to university

(v) exactly ten of all the chosen students go to university.

[MEI]

9 The probability that I dial a wrong number when making a telephone call is 0.015. In a typical week I will make 50 telephone calls. Using a Poisson approximation to a binomial model find, correct to two decimal places, the probability that in such a week

(i) I dial no wrong numbers

(ii) I dial more than two wrong numbers.

Comment on the suitability of the binomial model and of the Poisson approximation.

[Cambridge]

10 A Christmas draw aims to sell 5000 tickets, 50 of which will each win a prize.

(i) A syndicate buys 200 tickets. Let X represent the number of tickets that win a prize.

(a) Justify the use of the Poisson approximation for the distribution of X.

(b) Calculate $P(X \leqslant 3)$.

(ii) Calculate how many tickets should be bought in order for there to be a 90% probability of winning at least one prize.

[Cambridge]

11 A large number of screwdrivers from a trial production run is inspected. It is found that the cellulose acetate handles are defective on 1% and the chrome steel blades are defective on 1.5% of the screwdrivers, the defects occurring independently.

(i) What is the probability that a sample of 80 contains more than two defective screwdrivers?

(ii) What is the probability that a sample of 80 contains at least one screwdriver with both a defective handle and a defective blade?

[O & C]

Historical note

Simeon Poisson was born in Pithiviers in France in 1781. Under family pressure he began to study medicine but after some time gave it up for his real interest, mathematics. For the rest of his life Poisson lived and worked as a mathematician in Paris. His contribution to the subject spanned a broad range of topics in both pure and applied mathematics, including integration, electricity and magnetism and planetary orbits as well as statistics. He was the author of between 300 and 400 publications and originally derived the Poisson distribution as an approximation to the binomial distribution.

When he was a small boy, Poisson had his hands tied by his nanny who then hung him from a hook on the wall so that he could not get into trouble while she went out. In later life he devoted a lot of time to studying the motion of a pendulum and claimed that this interest derived from his childhood experience swinging against the wall.

1 A rare disease is being studied in a Manchester hospital. The disease occurs only in those who carry a particular gene, and then only if it is triggered by dietary factors. The number of carriers, n, is many thousands; the probability, p, of this disease being triggered in any carrier in any particular year is small. The values of n and p are unknown but, on average, there are 4.9 new cases per year reported in Manchester.

(i) State the distribution which would best model the occurrence of the disease if n and p were known. State also a suitable approximating distribution and explain briefly why it is suitable.

(ii) Show that it is very unlikely that a year will go by with no new cases of the disease reported in Manchester.

(iii) Find the probability that, in two years, 16 or more cases will be reported in Manchester.

(iv) A breakthrough in genetics suggests that in a city the size of Manchester n is about 23 000. Obtain a corresponding estimate of p.

[MEI]

2 In one part of the country, one person in 80 has blood of Type P. A random sample of 150 blood donors is chosen from that part of the country. Let X represent the number of donors in the sample having blood of Type P.

(i) State the distribution of X. Find the parameter of the Poisson distribution which can be used as an approximation. Give a reason why a Poisson approximation is appropriate.

(ii) Using the Poisson distribution, calculate the probability that in the sample of 150 donors at least two have blood of Type P.

(iii) A hospital urgently requires blood of Type P. How large a random sample of donors must be taken in order that the probability of finding at least one donor of Type P should be 0.99 or more?

[MEI, *part*]

3 A car hire firm has three cars, which it hires out on a daily basis. The number of cars demanded per day follows a Poisson distribution with mean 2.1.

(i) Find the probability that exactly two cars are hired out on any one day.

(ii) Find the probability that all cars are in use on any one day.

(iii) Find the probability that all cars are in use on exactly three days of a five-day week.

(iv) Find the probability that exactly ten cars are demanded in a five-day week. Explain whether or not such a demand could always be met.

(v) It costs the firm £20 a day to run each car, whether it is hired out or not. The daily hire charge per car is £50. Find the expected daily profit.

[MEI]

4 In Britain the average number of babies born per day is currently about 2040. In a recent study it has been estimated that one baby in 6000 is born with a certain rare disease. You may assume that this disease occurs randomly.

  (i) State the distribution which would best model the number of babies born per day with the disease. Explain why a Poisson distribution is a suitable approximation and state its parameter.

  (ii) Use the approximating distribution in part **(i)** to calculate the probability of exactly one baby being born with the disease on a particular day.

  (iii) Find the probability that, during the 30 days of April, 12 or more babies are born with the disease.

  (iv) The probability of k or fewer babies being born with the disease, during the month of April, is less than 10%. Find the greatest value of k.

  In fact, three babies with the disease were born during April. What light does this shed on the model?

  [MEI, *part*]

5 In Abbotston town centre, the number of incidents of criminal damage reported to the police averages two per week.

  (i) Explain why the Poisson distribution might be thought to be a suitable model for the number of incidents of criminal damage reported per week.

  (ii) Find the probabilities of the following events, according to the Poisson model.

   (a) Exactly two incidents are reported in a week.

   (b) Two consecutive weeks are incident-free.

   (c) More than ten incidents are reported in a period of four weeks.

  [MEI, *part*]

6 The number of incoming telephone calls received per minute by a company's telephone exchange follows a Poisson distribution with mean 1.92.

  (i) Find the probabilities of the following events.

   (a) Exactly two calls are received in a one-minute interval.

   (b) Exactly two calls are received each minute in a five-minute interval.

   (c) At least ten calls are received in a five-minute interval.

  The number of outgoing telephone calls made per minute at the same exchange also follows a Poisson distribution, with mean λ. It is found that the proportion of one-minute intervals containing no outgoing calls is 20%. Incoming and outgoing calls occur independently.

  (ii) Find the value of λ.

  (iii) Find the probability that a total of four calls, incoming and outgoing, pass through the exchange in a one-minute interval.

  (iv) Given that exactly four calls pass through the exchange in a one-minute interval, find the probability that two are incoming and two are outgoing.

  [MEI]

7   An airline regularly sells more seats for its early morning flight from London to Paris than are available. On average, 5% of customers who have purchased tickets do not turn up. For this flight, the airline always sells 108 tickets. Let X represent the number of customers who do not turn up for this flight.

   (i)   State the distribution of X, giving one assumption you must make for it to be appropriate.

   There is room for 104 passengers on the flight. For the rest of the question use a suitable Poisson approximation.

   (ii) Find the probability that
         (a) there are exactly three empty seats on Monday's flight
         (b) Tuesday's flight is full
         (c) from Monday to Friday inclusive the flight is full on just one day.

   If a customer turns up, but no seat is available, the airline pays compensation of £250.

   (iii) Calculate the expected amount of compensation per flight.

[MEI]

8   The numbers of goals per game scored by teams playing at home and away in the Premier League are modelled by independent Poisson distributions with means 1.63 and 1.17 respectively.

   (i)   Find the probability that, in a game chosen at random,
         (a) the home team scores at least two goals
         (b) the result is a 1–1 draw
         (c) the teams score five goals between them.
   (ii) Give two reasons why the proposed model might not be suitable.

[MEI, *part*]

9   The manufacturers of *Jupiter Jellybabies* have launched a promotion to boost sales. One per cent of bags, chosen at random, contains a prize. A school tuck-shop takes delivery of 500 bags of *Jupiter Jellybabies*. Let X represent the number of bags in the delivery which contain a prize.

   (i)   State clearly the distribution which X takes.
   (ii) Using a Poisson approximating distribution, find $P(3 \leqslant X \leqslant 7)$.

   The values of the prizes are in the following proportions.

Value of prize	£10	£100	£1000
Proportion	90%	9%	1%

   (iii) Suppose the tuck-shop receives five bags which contain prizes. Find the probability that at least one of these prizes has value £1000.

[MEI, *part*]

10 Every day I check the number of emails on my computer at home. The numbers of emails, x, received per day for a random sample of 100 days are summarised by

$$\sum x = 184, \qquad \sum x^2 = 514.$$

(i) Find the mean and variance of the data.

(ii) Give two reasons why the Poisson distribution might be thought to be a suitable model for the number of emails received per day.

(iii) Using the mean as found in part **(i)**, calculate the expected number of days, in a period of 100 days, on which I will receive exactly two emails.

On a working day, I also receive emails at the office. The number of emails received per day at the office follows a Poisson distribution with mean λ. On 1.5% of working days I receive no emails at the office.

(iv) Show that $\lambda = 4.2$, correct to 2 significant figures. Hence find the probability that on one working day I receive at least five emails at the office.

(v) Find the probability that on one working day I receive a total of ten emails (at home and at the office).

[MEI, *part*]

11 A long-distance rail journey is scheduled to take five hours. Recent records show that trains completing this journey arrive late on 4% of occasions. Let X represent the number of times the train is late out of n journeys.

(i) State the distribution of X, giving an assumption you have to make for it to be valid. Under what condition would a Poisson approximation be suitable?

You are given that 27 such journeys occur per week.

(ii) Use a Poisson approximation to calculate the probability of exactly five late arrivals during the next four weeks. You are given that, using the exact distribution of X, $P(X = 5) = 0.1704$, correct to 4 significant figures. Calculate the percentage error in using the corresponding Poisson approximation.

The remaining parts of this question refer to a period of ten weeks. In these parts, use a suitable Poisson approximation.

(iii) Find the probability that between 8 and 12 (inclusive) journeys result in a late arrival.

(iv) Find the smallest value of k such that $P(X > k)$ is less than 5%. How many late arrivals do you think the rail 'watchdog' would tolerate before a significant deterioration in punctuality was detected? Give reasons for your answers.

[MEI]

12 Recently our local health centre claimed that 95% of adults who have a flu jab during October do not catch flu during the next six months.

In parts **(i)** to **(iv)**, assume that this claim is true and that people catch flu independently of each other.

(i) Find the probability that, of 25 adults given a flu jab, just two catch flu within the next six months.

During October, the health centre gave a flu jab to 184 adults.

(ii) Write down the parameter of an approximating Poisson distribution that describes the number of people who catch flu within six months. Explain briefly why this is a suitable approximation.

(iii) Find the probability of more than ten of those given flu jabs catching flu.

(iv) Find the least integer k such that the probability of k or more adults catching flu is less than 5%.

(v) In fact, 20 of the adults given flu jabs in October catch flu during the next six months. What does this suggest about the assumptions made earlier?

[MEI]

13 A factory has a large number of lights in it. Records are kept of the number of light bulbs which need to be replaced each day. The figures for a random sample of 100 days are as follows.

Number of light bulbs, x	0	1	2	3	4	5	6	7+
Number of days, f	14	10	15	34	11	12	4	0

(i) Explain why the Poisson distribution might be thought to be a suitable model for the number of light bulbs which need to be replaced per day.

(ii) Find the mean and variance of the given data. Hence give an additional reason for supposing that the Poisson model might be appropriate.

(iii) Using the mean calculated in part **(ii)**, calculate the expected frequencies corresponding to the given frequencies in the table. Comment further on the suitability of the Poisson model.

(iv) *Assuming that the Poisson model is appropriate*, write down the distribution for the number of light bulbs which need to be changed in a working year of 250 days. Give two distinct reasons why it might not be practical to use this distribution for calculating probabilities.

[MEI]

1 **The Poisson probability distribution**

If $X \sim$ Poisson (λ) the parameter $\lambda > 0$.

$$P(X = r) = e^{-\lambda}\frac{\lambda^r}{r!} \quad r \geqslant 0,\ r \text{ is an integer}$$

$$E(X) = \lambda$$

$$\text{Var}(X) = \lambda$$

2 **Conditions under which the Poisson distribution may be used**
- The Poisson distribution is generally thought of as the probability distribution for the number of occurrences of a *rare event*.
- Situations in which the mean number of occurrences is known (or can easily be found) but in which it is not possible, or even meaningful, to give values to n or p may be modelled using the Poisson distribution provided that the occurrences are
  — random
  — independent.

3 **The sum of two Poisson distributions**

If $X \sim$ Poisson (λ), $Y \sim$ Poisson (μ) and X and Y are independent

$$X + Y \sim \text{Poisson } (\lambda + \mu).$$

4 **Approximating to the binomial distribution**

The Poisson distribution may be used as an approximation to the binomial distribution, $B(n, p)$, when
— n is large
— p is small (and so the event is rare)
— np is not large.

It would be unusual to use the Poisson distribution with parameter, λ, greater than about 20.

The Normal distribution

2

The
Normal
law of error
stands out in the
experience of mankind
as one of the broadest
generalisations of natural
philosophy. It serves as the
guiding instrument in researches
in the physical and social sciences
and in medicine, agriculture and engineering.
It is an indispensable tool for the analysis and the
interpretation of the basic data obtained by observation and experiment.

W. J. Youden

THE AVONFORD STAR

VILLAGERS GET GIANT BOBBY

The good people of Middle Fishbrook have special reason to be good these days. Since last week, their daily lives are being watched over by their new village bobby, Wilf 'Shorty' Harris.

At 195 cm, Wilf is the tallest policeman in the country. 'I don't expect any trouble', says Wilf. 'But I wouldn't advise anyone to tangle with me on a dark night.'

Seeing Wilf towering above me, I decided that most people would prefer not to put his words to the test.

Towering bobby, Wilf 'Shorty' Harris, is bound to deter mischief in Middle Fishbrook

Wilf Harris is clearly exceptionally tall, but how much so? Is he one in a hundred, or a thousand or even a million? To answer that question you need to know the distribution of heights of adult British men.

The first point that needs to be made is that height is a continuous variable and not a discrete one. If you measure accurately enough it can take any value.

This means that it does not really make sense to ask 'What is the probability that somebody chosen at random has height exactly 195 cm?' The answer is zero.

However, you can ask questions like 'What is the probability that somebody chosen at random has height between 194 cm and 196 cm?' and 'What is the probability that somebody chosen at random has height at least 195 cm?'. When the variable is continuous, you are concerned with a range of values rather than a single value.

Like many other naturally occurring variables, the heights of adult men may be modelled by a Normal distribution, shown in figure 2.1. You will see that this has a distinctive bell-shaped curve and is symmetrical about its middle. The curve is continuous as height is a continuous variable.

On figure 2.1, area represents probability so the shaded area to the right of 195 cm represents the probability that a randomly selected adult male is over 195 cm tall.

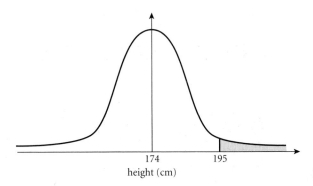

Figure 2.1

Before you can start to find this area, you must know the mean and standard deviation of the distribution, in this case about 174 cm and 7 cm respectively.

So Wilf's height is 195 cm − 174 cm = 21 cm above the mean, and that is

$$\frac{21}{7} = 3 \text{ standard deviations.}$$

The number of standard deviations beyond the mean, in this case 3, is denoted by the letter z. Thus the shaded area gives the probability of obtaining a value of $z \geqslant 3$.

You find this area by looking up the value of $\Phi(z)$ when $z = 3$ in a Normal distribution table of $\Phi(z)$ as shown in figure 2.2, and then calculating $1 - \Phi(z)$. (Φ is the Greek letter phi.)

ADD

z	.00	.01	.02	.03	.04	.05	.06	.07	.08	.09	1 2 3 4 5 6 7 8 9
0.0	.5000	5040	5080	5120	5160	5199	5239	5279	5319	5359	4 8 12 16 20 24 28 32 36
0.1	.5398	5438	5478	5517	5557	5596	5636	5675	5714	5753	4 8 12 16 20 24 28 32 35
0.2	.5793	5832	5871	5910	5948	5987	6026	6064	6103	6141	4 8 12 15 19 23 27 31 35
0.3	.6179	6217	6255	6293	6331	6368	6406	6443	6480	6517	4 8 11 15 19 23 26 30 34
0.4	.6554	6591	6628	6664	6700	6736	6772	6808	6844	6879	4 7 11 14 18 22 25 29 32
0.5	.6915	6950	6985	7019	7054	7088	7123	7157	7190	7224	3 7 10 14 17 21 24 27 31
0.6	.7257	7291	7324	7357	7389	7422	7454	7486	7517	7549	3 6 10 13 16 19 23 26 29
0.7	.7580	7611	7642	7673	7704	7734	7764	7794	7823	7852	3 6 9 12 15 18 21 24 27
0.8	.7881	7910	7939	7967	7995	8023	8051	8078	8106	8133	3 6 8 11 14 17 19 22 25
3.0	.9987	9987	9988	9988	9988	9989	9989	9989	9990	9990	
3.1	.9990	9991	9991	9991	9992	9992	9992	9992	9993	9993	*differences*
3.2	.9993	9993	9994	9994	9994	9994	9994	9995	9995	9995	*untrustworthy*
3.3	.9995	9995	9996	9996	9996	9996	9996	9996	9996	9997	
3.4	.9997	9997	9997	9997	9997	9997	9997	9997	9997	9998	

$\Phi(3) = .9987$

Figure 2.2 Extract from tables of $\Phi(z)$

This gives $\Phi(3) = 0.9987$, and so $1 - \Phi(3) = 0.0013$.

The probability of a randomly selected adult male being 195 cm or over is 0.0013. Slightly more than one man in a thousand is at least as tall as Wilf.

Using Normal distribution tables

The function $\Phi(z)$ gives the area under the Normal distribution curve to the *left* of the value z, that is the shaded area in figure 2.3 (it is the cumulative distribution function). The total area under the curve is 1, and the area given by $\Phi(z)$ represents the probability of a value smaller than z.

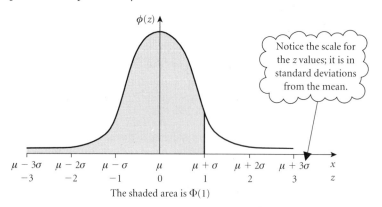

Notice the scale for the z values; it is in standard deviations from the mean.

The shaded area is $\Phi(1)$

Figure 2.3

If the variable X has mean μ and standard deviation σ then x, a particular value of X, is transformed into z by the equation

$$z = \frac{x - \mu}{\sigma}.$$

z is a particular value of the variable Z which has mean 0 and standard deviation 1 and is the *standardised* form of the Normal distribution.

	Actual distribution, X	Standardised distribution, Z
Mean	μ	0
Standard deviation	σ	1
Particular value	x	$z = \dfrac{x - \mu}{\sigma}$

Notice how lower case letters, x and z, are used to indicate particular values of the random variables, whereas upper case letters, X and Z, are used to describe or name those variables.

Normal distribution tables are easy to use but you should always make a point of drawing a diagram and shading the region you are interested in.

It is often helpful to know that in a Normal distribution, roughly

- 68% of the values lie within ± 1 standard deviation of the mean
- 95% of the values lie within ± 2 standard deviations of the mean
- 99.75% of the values lie within ± 3 standard deviations of the mean.

EXAMPLE 2.1

Assuming the distribution of the heights of adult men is Normal, with mean 174 cm and standard deviation 7 cm, find the probability that a randomly selected adult man is

(i) under 185 cm
(ii) over 185 cm
(iii) over 180 cm
(iv) between 180 cm and 185 cm
(v) under 170 cm

giving your answers to 2 significant figures.

SOLUTION

The mean height, $\mu = 174$.

The standard deviation, $\sigma = 7$.

(i) The probability that an adult man selected at random is under 185 cm.

The area required is that shaded in figure 2.4 overleaf.

$$x = 185\,\text{cm}$$

and so $\qquad z = \dfrac{185 - 174}{7} = 1.571$

$$\Phi(1.571) = 0.9419$$

$$= 0.94 \quad (2\ \text{s.f.})$$

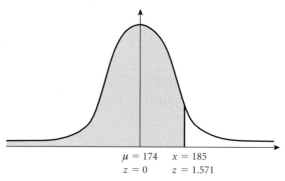

Figure 2.4

Answer: The probability that an adult man selected at random is under 185 cm is 0.94.

(ii) The probability that an adult man selected at random is over 185 cm.

The area required is the complement of that for part **(i)**.

$$\text{Probability} = 1 - \Phi(1.571)$$

$$= 1 - 0.9419$$

$$= 0.0581$$

$$= 0.058 \quad (2\ \text{s.f.})$$

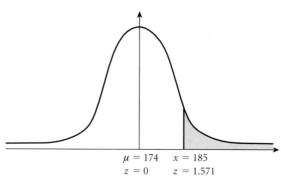

Figure 2.5

Answer: The probability that an adult man selected at random is over 185 cm is 0.058.

(iii) The probability that an adult man selected at random is over 180 cm.

$$x = 180 \quad \text{and so} \quad z = \frac{180 - 174}{7} = 0.857$$

The area required $= 1 - \Phi(0.857)$

$$= 1 - 0.8042$$
$$= 0.1958$$
$$= 0.20 \quad (2 \text{ s.f.})$$

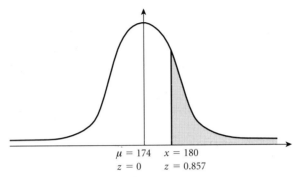

$$\mu = 174 \quad x = 180$$
$$z = 0 \quad z = 0.857$$

Figure 2.6

Answer: The probability that an adult man selected at random is over 180 cm is 0.20.

(iv) The probability that an adult man selected at random is between 180 cm and 185 cm.

The required area is shown in figure 2.7. It is

$$\Phi(1.571) - \Phi(0.857) = 0.9419 - 0.8042$$
$$= 0.1377$$
$$= 0.14 \quad (2 \text{ s.f.})$$

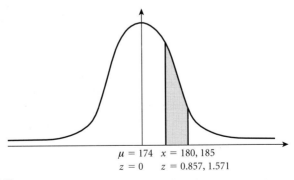

$$\mu = 174 \quad x = 180, 185$$
$$z = 0 \quad z = 0.857, 1.571$$

Figure 2.7

Answer: The probability that an adult man selected at random is over 180 cm but under 185 cm is 0.14.

(v) The probability that an adult man selected at random is under 170 cm.

In this case $x = 170$

and so $z = \dfrac{170 - 174}{7} = -0.571$

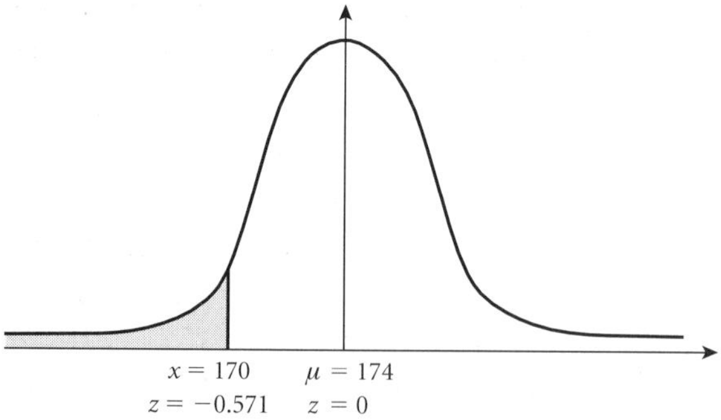

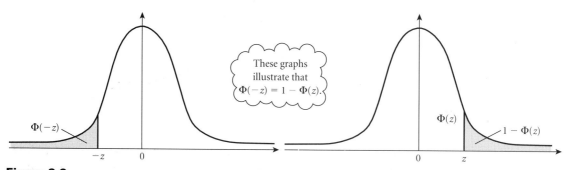

$$x = 170 \qquad \mu = 174$$
$$z = -0.571 \qquad z = 0$$

Figure 2.8

However when you come to look up $\Phi(-0.571)$, you will find that only positive values of z are given in your tables. You overcome this problem by using the symmetry of the Normal curve. The area you want in this case is that to the left of -0.571 and this is clearly just the same as that to the right of $+0.571$ (see figure 2.9).

So $\Phi(-0.571) = 1 - \Phi(0.571)$

$$= 1 - 0.716$$
$$= 0.284$$
$$= 0.28 \quad (2\ \text{s.f.})$$

These graphs illustrate that $\Phi(-z) = 1 - \Phi(z)$.

$\Phi(-z)$ $-z$ 0 $\Phi(z)$ 0 z $1 - \Phi(z)$

Figure 2.9

Answer: The probability that an adult man selected at random is under 170 cm is 0.28.

The Normal curve

All Normal curves have the same basic shape, so that by scaling the two axes suitably you can always fit one Normal curve exactly on top of another one.

The curve for the Normal distribution with mean μ and standard deviation σ (i.e. variance σ^2) is given by the function $\phi(x)$ in

$$\phi(x) = \frac{1}{\sigma\sqrt{2\pi}}\, e^{-\frac{1}{2}\left(\frac{x-\mu}{\sigma}\right)^2}$$

The notation $N(\mu, \sigma^2)$ is used to describe this distribution. The mean, μ, and standard deviation, σ (or variance, σ^2), are the two parameters used to define the distribution. Once you know their values, you know everything there is to know about the distribution. The standardised variable Z has mean 0 and variance 1, so its distribution is $N(0, 1)$.

After the variable X has been transformed to Z using $z = \dfrac{x - \mu}{\sigma}$ the form of the curve (now standardised) becomes

$$\phi(z) = \frac{1}{\sqrt{2\pi}}\, e^{-\frac{1}{2}z^2}$$

However, the exact shape of the Normal curve is often less useful than the area underneath it, which represents a probability. For example, the probability that $Z \leqslant 2$ is given by the shaded area in figure 2.10.

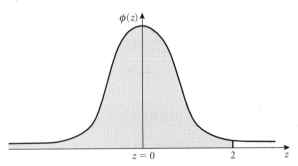

Figure 2.10

Easy though it looks, the function $\phi(z)$ cannot be integrated algebraically to find the area under the curve; this can only be found by using a numerical method. The values found by doing so are given as a table and this area function is called $\Phi(z)$.

EXAMPLE 2.2

Skilled operators make a particular component for an engine. The company believes that the time taken to make this component may be modelled by the Normal distribution with mean 95 minutes and standard deviation 4 minutes.

Assuming the company's belief to be true, find the probability that the time taken to make one of these components, selected at random, was

(i) over 97 minutes
(ii) under 90 minutes
(iii) between 90 and 97 minutes.

Sheila believes that the company is allowing too long for the job and invites them to time her. They find that only 10% of the components take her over 90 minutes to make, and that 20% take her less than 70 minutes.

(iv) Estimate the mean and standard deviation of the time Sheila takes.

SOLUTION

According to the company $\mu = 95$ and $\sigma = 4$ so the distribution is $N(95, 4^2)$.

(i) The probability that a component required over 97 minutes

$$z = \frac{97 - 95}{4} = 0.5$$

The probability is represented by the shaded area and given by

$$1 - \Phi(0.5) = 1 - 0.6915$$
$$= 0.3085$$
$$= 0.31 \quad (2 \text{ d.p.})$$

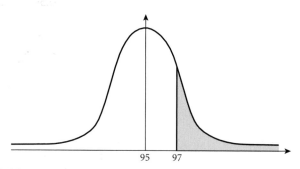

95   97

Figure 2.11

Answer: The probability it took the operator over 97 minutes to manufacture a randomly selected component is 0.31.

(ii) The probability that a component required under 90 minutes

$$z = \frac{90 - 95}{4} = -1.25$$

The probability is represented by the shaded area and given by

$$1 - \Phi(1.25) = 1 - 0.8944$$
$$= 0.1056$$
$$= 0.11 \quad (2 \text{ d.p.})$$

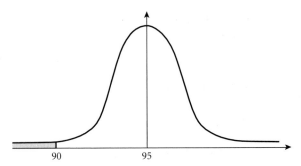

Figure 2.12

Answer: The probability it took the operator under 90 minutes to manufacture a randomly selected component is 0.11.

(iii) The probability that a component required between 90 and 97 minutes

The probability is represented by the shaded area and given by

$$1 - 0.1056 - 0.3085 = 0.5859$$
$$= 0.59 \quad (2 \text{ d.p.})$$

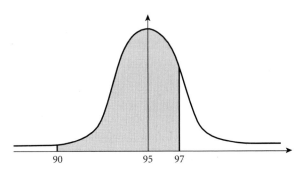

Figure 2.13

Answer: The probability it took the operator between 90 and 97 minutes to manufacture a randomly selected component is 0.59.

(iv) Estimate the mean and standard deviation of the time Sheila takes.

The question has now been put the other way round. You have to infer the mean, μ, and standard deviation, σ, from the areas under different parts of the graph.

10% take her 90 minutes or more. This means that the shaded area is 0.1.

$$z = \frac{90 - \mu}{\sigma}$$

$$\Phi(z) = 1 - 0.1 = 0.9$$

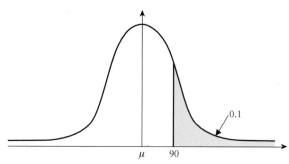

Figure 2.14

You must now use the table of the inverse Normal function, $\Phi^{-1}(p) = z$ which tells you $z = 1.282$.

The inverse Normal function – values of $\Phi^{-1}(p) = z$

p	.000	.001	.002	.003	.004	.005	.006	.007	.008	.009
.50	.0000	.0025	.0050	.0075	.0100	.0125	.0150	.0175	.0201	.0226
.51	.0251	.0276	.0301	.0326	.0351	.0376	.0401	.0426	.0451	.0476
.52	.0502	.0527	.0552	.0577	.0602	.0627	.0652	.0677	.0702	.0728
.89	1.227	1.232	1.237	1.243	1.248	1.254	1.259	1.265	1.270	1.276
.90	1.282	1.287	1.293	1.299	1.305	1.311	1.317	1.323	1.329	1.335
.91	1.341	1.347	1.353	1.360	1.366	1.372	1.379	1.385	1.392	1.398
.92	1.405	1.412	1.419	1.426	1.433	1.440	1.447	1.454	1.461	1.468

$\Phi^{-1}(0.9) = 1.282$

Figure 2.15 Extract from the inverse Normal distribution table

If you do not have the table of the inverse Normal function, you can find the same answer by using the table of $\Phi(z) = p$ in reverse.

z	.00	.01	.02	.03	.04	.05	.06	.07	.08	.09	1	2	3	4	5	6	7	8	9
0.0	.5000	5040	5080	5120	5160	5199	5239	5279	5319	5359	4	8	12	16	20	24	28	32	36
0.1	.5398	5438	5478	5517	5557	5596	5636	5675	5714	5753	4	8	12	16	20	24	28	32	35
0.2	.5793	5832	5871	5910	5948	5987	6026	6064	6103	6141	4	8	12	15	19	23	27	31	35
0.3	.6179	6217	6255	6293	6331	6368	6406	6443	6480	6517	4	8	11	15	19	23	26	30	34
0.4	.6554	6591	6628	6664	6700	6736	6772	6808	6844	6879	4	7	11	14	18	22	25	29	32
0.5	.6915	6950	6985	7019	7054	7088	7123	7157	7190	7224	3	7	10	14	17	21	24	27	31
0.6	.7257	7291	7324	7357	7389	7422	7454	7486	7517	7549	3	6	10	13	16	19	23	26	29
0.7	.7580	7611	7642	7673	7704	7734	7764	7794	7823	7852	3	6	9	12	15	18	21	24	27
0.8	.7881	7910	7939	7967	7995	8023	8051	8078	8106	8133	3	6	8	11	14	17	19	22	25
0.9	.8159	8186	8212	8238	8264	8289	8315	8340	8365	8389	3	5	8	10	13	15	18	20	23
1.0	.8413	8438	8461	8485	8508	8531	8554	8577	8599	8621	2	5	7	9	12	14	16	18	21
1.1	.8643	8665	8686	8708	8729	8749	8770	8790	8810	8830	2	4	6	8	10	12	14	16	19
1.2	.8849	8869	8888	8907	8925	8944	8962	8980	8997	9015	2	4	6	7	9	11	13	15	16
1.3	.9032	9049	9066	9082	9099	9115	9131	9147	9162	9177	2	3	5	6	8	10	11	13	14
1.4	.9192	9207	9222	9236	9251	9265	9279	9292	9306	9319	1	3	4	6	7	8	10	11	13

$\Phi^{-1}(0.9) = 1.2815$

Figure 2.16 Extract from tables of $\Phi(z)$

Returning to the problem, you now know that

$$\frac{90 - \mu}{\sigma} = 1.282 \qquad \Rightarrow \qquad 90 - \mu = 1.282\sigma.$$

The second piece of information, that 20% of components took Sheila under 70 minutes, is illustrated in figure 2.17.

$$z = \frac{70 - \mu}{\sigma}$$

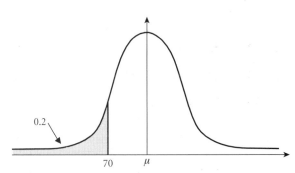

Figure 2.17

(z has a negative value in this case, the point being to the left of the mean.)

$$\Phi(z) = 0.2$$

and so, by symmetry,

$$\Phi(-z) = 1 - 0.2 = 0.8.$$

Using the table of the inverse Normal function gives

$$-z = 0.8416 \quad \text{or} \quad z = -0.8416$$

This gives a second equation for μ and σ.

$$\frac{70 - \mu}{\sigma} = -0.8416 \qquad \Rightarrow \qquad 70 - \mu = -0.8416\sigma$$

You now solve the two simultaneous equations

$$90 - \mu = 1.282\sigma$$
$$70 - \mu = -0.8416\sigma$$

Subtract $20 \quad = \quad 2.1236\sigma \qquad \sigma = 9.418 = 9.4 \quad \text{(1 d.p.)}$

and $\qquad \mu = 77.926 = 77.9 \quad \text{(1 d.p.)}$

Answer: Sheila's mean time is 77.9 minutes with standard deviation 9.4 minutes.

1 The distribution of the heights of 18-year-old girls may be modelled by the Normal distribution with mean 162.5 cm and standard deviation 6 cm. Find the probability that the height of a randomly selected 18-year-old girl is
(i) under 168.5 cm
(ii) over 174.5 cm
(iii) between 168.5 and 174.5 cm.

2 A pet shop has a tank of goldfish for sale. All the fish in the tank were hatched at the same time and their weights may be taken to be Normally distributed with mean 100 g and standard deviation 10 g. Melanie is buying a goldfish and is invited to catch the one she wants in a small net. In fact the fish are much too quick for her to be able to catch any particular one and the fish which she eventually nets is selected at random. Find the probability that its weight is
(i) over 115 g
(ii) under 105 g
(iii) between 105 and 115 g.

3 When he makes instant coffee, Tony puts a spoonful of powder into a mug. The weight of coffee in grams on the spoon may be modelled by the Normal distribution with mean 5 g and standard deviation 1 g. If he uses more than 6.5 g Julia complains that it is too strong and if he uses less than 4 g she tells him it is too weak. Find the probability that he makes the coffee
(i) too strong
(ii) too weak
(iii) all right.

4 When a butcher takes an order for a Christmas turkey, he asks the customer what weight in kilograms the bird should be. He then sends his order to a turkey farmer who supplies birds of about the requested weight. For any particular weight of bird ordered, the error in kilograms may be taken to be Normally distributed with mean 0 kg and standard deviation 0.75 kg.

Mrs Jones orders a 10 kg turkey from the butcher. Find the probability that the one she gets is

(i) over 12 kg

(ii) under 10 kg

(iii) within 0.5 kg of the weight she actually ordered.

5 A biologist finds a nesting colony of a previously unknown sea bird on a remote island. She is able to take measurements on 100 of the eggs before replacing them in their nests. She records their weights, w g, in this frequency table.

Weight, w	$25 < w \leqslant 27$	$27 < w \leqslant 29$	$29 < w \leqslant 31$	$31 < w \leqslant 33$	$33 < w \leqslant 35$	$35 < w \leqslant 37$
Frequency	2	13	35	33	17	0

(i) Find the mean and standard deviation of these data.

(ii) Assuming the weights of the eggs for this type of bird are Normally distributed and that their mean and standard deviation are the same as those of this sample, find how many eggs you would expect to be in each of these categories.

(iii) Do you think the assumption that the weights of the eggs are Normally distributed is reasonable?

6 The length of life of a certain make of tyre is Normally distributed about a mean of 24 000 km with a standard deviation of 2500 km.

(i) What percentage of such tyres will need replacing before they have travelled 20 000 km?

(ii) As a result of improvements in manufacture, the length of life is still Normally distributed, but the proportion of tyres failing before 20 000 km is reduced to 1.5%.

(a) If the standard deviation has remained unchanged, calculate the new mean length of life.

(b) If, instead, the mean length of life has remained unchanged, calculate the new standard deviation.

[MEI]

7 A machine is set to produce nails of lengths 10 cm, with standard deviation 0.05 cm. The lengths of the nails are Normally distributed.

  (i) Find the percentage of nails produced between 9.95 cm and 10.08 cm in length.

The machine's setting is moved by a careless apprentice with the consequence that 16% of the nails are under 5.2 cm in length and 20% are over 5.3 cm.

  (ii) Find the new mean and standard deviation.

8 The weights of eggs, measured in grams, can be modelled by a N(85.0, 36.0) distribution. Eggs are classified as large, medium or small, where a large egg weighs 90.0 grams or more, and 25% of eggs are classified as small. Calculate

  (i) the percentage of eggs which are classified as large

  (ii) the maximum weight of a small egg.

[Cambridge]

9 The concentration by volume of methane at a point on the centre line of a jet of natural gas mixing with air is distributed approximately Normally with mean 20% and standard deviation 7%. Find the probabilities that the concentration

  (i) exceeds 30%

  (ii) is between 5% and 15%.

  (iii) In another similar jet, the mean concentration is 18% and the standard deviation is 5%. Find the probability that in at least one of the jets the concentration is between 5% and 15%.

[MEI]

10 In a particular experiment, the length of a metal bar is measured many times. The measured values are distributed approximately Normally with mean 1.340 m and standard deviation 0.021 m. Find the probabilities that any one measured value

  (i) exceeds 1.370 m.

  (ii) lies between 1.310 m and 1.370 m.

  (iii) lies between 1.330 m and 1.390 m.

  (iv) Find the length l for which the probability that any one measured value is less than l is 0.1.

[MEI]

11 Each weekday a man goes to work by bus. His arrival time at the bus stop is Normally distributed with standard deviation 3 minutes. His mean arrival time is 8.30 am. Buses leave promptly every 5 minutes at 8.21 am, 8.26 am, etc. Find the probabilities that he catches the bus at

(i) 8.26 am　　　　**(ii)** 8.31 am　　　　**(iii)** 8.36 am

assuming that he always gets on the first bus to arrive.

(iv) The man is late for work if he catches a bus after 8.31 am. What mean arrival time would ensure that, on average, he is not late for work more than one day in five? [Assume that he cannot change the standard deviation of his arrival time and give your answer to the nearest 10 s.]

[MEI]

12 A machine is used to fill cans of soup with a nominal volume of 0.450 litres. Suppose that the machine delivers a quantity of soup which is Normally distributed with mean μ litres and standard deviation σ litres. Given that $\mu = 0.457$ and $\sigma = 0.004$, find the probability that a randomly chosen can contains less than the nominal volume.

It is required by law that no more than 1% of cans contain less than the nominal volume. Find

(i) the least value of μ which will comply with the law when $\sigma = 0.004$

(ii) the greatest value of σ which will comply with the law when $\mu = 0.457$.

[MEI]

13 A factory is lit by a large number of electric light bulbs whose lifetimes are modelled by a Normal distribution with mean 1000 hours and standard deviation 110 hours. Operating conditions require that all bulbs are on continuously.

(i) What proportions of bulbs have lifetimes that

　　(a) exceed 950 hours　　　**(b)** exceed 1050 hours?

(ii) Given that a bulb has already lasted 950 hours, what is the probability that it will last a further 100 hours?

Give all answers correct to 3 decimal places.

The factory management is to adopt a policy whereby all bulbs will be replaced periodically after a fixed interval.

(iii) To the nearest day, how long should this interval be if, on average, 1% of the bulbs are to burn out between successive replacement times?

[MEI]

14 A factory produces a very large number of steel bars. The lengths of these bars are Normally distributed with 33% of them measuring 20.06 cm or more and 12% of them measuring 20.02 cm or less.

Write down two simultaneous equations for the mean and standard deviation of the distribution and solve to find values to 4 significant figures. Hence estimate the proportion of steel bars which measure 20.03 cm or more.

The bars are acceptable if they measure between 20.02 cm and 20.08 cm. What percentage are rejected as being outside the acceptable range?

[MEI]

15 The diameters D of screws made in a factory are Normally distributed with mean 1 mm. Given that 10% of the screws have diameters greater than 1.04 mm, find the standard deviation correct to 3 significant figures, and hence show that about 2.7% of the screws have diameters greater than 1.06 mm.

Find, correct to 2 significant figures,
(i) the number d for which 99% of the screws have diameters that exceed d mm
(ii) the number e for which 99% of the screws have diameters that do not differ from the mean by more than e mm.

[MEI]

16 A machine produces crankshafts whose diameters are Normally distributed with mean 5 cm and standard deviation 0.03 cm. Find the percentage of crankshafts it will produce whose diameters lie between 4.95 cm and 4.97 cm.

What is the probability that two successive crankshafts will both have a diameter in this interval?

Crankshafts with diameters outside the interval 5 ± 0.05 cm are rejected. If the mean diameter of the machine's production remains unchanged, to what must the standard deviation be reduced if only 4% of the production is to be rejected?

[MEI]

Modelling discrete situations

Although the Normal distribution applies strictly to a continuous variable, it is also common to use it in situations where the variable is discrete providing that

- the distribution is approximately Normal; this requires that the steps in its possible values are small compared with its standard deviation
- *continuity corrections* are applied where appropriate.

The meaning of the term continuity correction is explained in the following example.

EXAMPLE 2.3

The result of an Intelligence Quotient (IQ) test is an integer score, X. Tests are designed so that X has a mean value of 100 with standard deviation 15. A large number of people have their IQs tested. What proportion of them would you expect to have IQs measuring between 106 and 110 (inclusive)?

SOLUTION

Although the random variable X is an integer and hence discrete, the steps of 1 in its possible values are small compared with the standard deviation of 15. So it is reasonable to treat it as if it is continuous.

If you assume that an IQ test is measuring innate, natural intelligence (rather than the results of learning), then it is reasonable to assume a Normal distribution.

If you draw the probability distribution function for the discrete variable X it looks like figure 2.18. The area you require is the total of the five bars representing 106, 107, 108, 109 and 110.

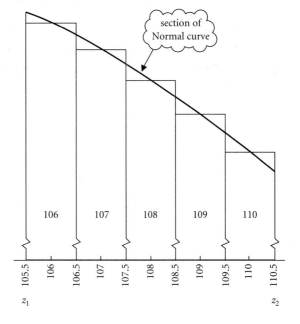

Figure 2.18

The equivalent section of the Normal curve would run not from 106 to 110 but from 105.5 to 110.5, as you can see in figure 2.18. When you change from the discrete scale to the continuous scale, the numbers 106, 107, etc. no longer represent the whole intervals, just their centre points.

So the area you require under the Normal curve is given by $\Phi(z_2) - \Phi(z_1)$

where $z_1 = \dfrac{105.5 - 100}{15}$ and $z_2 = \dfrac{110.5 - 100}{15}$.

This is $\Phi(0.7000) - \Phi(0.3667)$
$$= 0.7580 - 0.6431 = 0.1149$$

Answer: The proportion of IQs between 106 and 110 (inclusive) should be approximately 11%.

In this calculation, both end values needed to be adjusted to allow for the fact that a continuous distribution was being used to approximate a discrete one. These adjustments, $106 \rightarrow 105.5$ and $110 \rightarrow 110.5$, are called continuity corrections. Whenever a discrete distribution is approximated by a continuous one a continuity correction may need to be used.

You must always think carefully when applying a continuity correction. Should the corrections be added or subtracted? In this case 106 and 110 are inside the required area and so any value (like 105.7 or 110.4) which would round to them must be included. It is often helpful to draw a sketch to illustrate the region you want, like the one in figure 2.18.

If the region of interest is given in terms of inequalities, you should look carefully to see whether they are inclusive ($\leqslant$ or $\geqslant$) or exclusive ($<$ or $>$). For example $20 \leqslant X \leqslant 30$ becomes $19.5 \leqslant X < 30.5$ whereas $20 < X < 30$ becomes $20.5 \leqslant X < 29.5$.

Two particularly common situations are when the Normal distribution is used to approximate the binomial and the Poisson distributions.

Approximating the binomial distribution

You may use the Normal distribution as an approximation for the binomial, $B(n, p)$ (where n is the number of trials each having probability p of success) when

- n is large
- p is not too close to 0 or 1.

These conditions ensure that the distribution is reasonably symmetrical and not skewed away from either end, see figure 2.19.

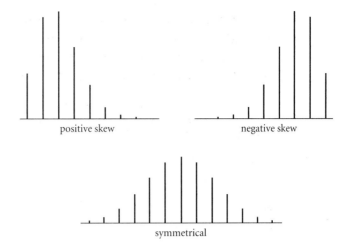

positive skew

negative skew

symmetrical

Figure 2.19

The parameters for the Normal distribution are then

Mean: $\mu = np$

Variance: $\sigma^2 = npq$

so that it can be denoted by $N(np, npq)$.

EXAMPLE 2.4

This is a true story. During voting at a by-election, an exit poll of 1700 voters indicated that 50% of people had voted for the Labour party candidate. When the votes were counted it was found that he had in fact received 57% support.

850 of the 1700 people interviewed said they had voted Labour but 57% of 1700 is 969, a much higher number. What went wrong? Is it possible to be so far out just by being unlucky and asking the wrong people?

SOLUTION

The situation of selecting a sample of 1700 people and asking them if they voted for one party or not is one that is modelled by the binomial distribution, in this case $B(1700, 0.57)$.

In theory you could multiply out $(0.43 + 0.57t)^{1700}$ and use that to find the probabilities of getting $0, 1, 2, \ldots, 850$ Labour voters in your sample of 1700. In practice such a method would be impractical because of the work involved.

What you can do is to use a Normal approximation. The required conditions are fulfilled: at 1700, n is certainly not small; $p = 0.57$ is near neither 0 nor 1.

The parameters for the Normal approximation are given by

$$\mu = np = 1700 \times 0.57 = 969$$
$$\sigma = \sqrt{npq} = \sqrt{1700 \times 0.57 \times 0.43} = 20.4$$

You will see that the standard deviation, 20.4, is large compared with the steps of 1 in the possible values of Labour voters.

The probability of getting no more than 850 Labour voters, $P(X \leqslant 850)$, is given by $\Phi(z)$, where

$$z = \frac{850.5 - 969}{20.4} = -5.8$$

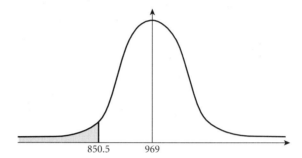

Figure 2.20

(Notice the continuity correction making 850 into 850.5.)

This is beyond the range of most tables and corresponds to a probability of about 0.000 01. The probability of a result as extreme as this is thus 0.000 02 (allowing for an equivalent result in the tail above the mean). It is clearly so unlikely that this was a result of random sampling that another explanation must be found.

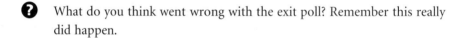

❓ What do you think went wrong with the exit poll? Remember this really did happen.

Approximating the Poisson distribution

You may use the Normal distribution as an approximation for the Poisson distribution, provided that its parameter (mean) λ is sufficiently large for the distribution to be reasonably symmetrical and not positively skewed.

As a working rule λ should be at least 10.

If $\lambda = 10$, mean $= 10$

and standard deviation $= \sqrt{10} = 3.16$.

A Normal distribution is almost entirely contained within 3 standard deviations of its mean and in this case the value 0 is slightly more than 3 standard deviations away from the mean value of 10.

The parameters for the Normal distribution are then

Mean: $\mu = \lambda$

Variance: $\sigma^2 = \lambda$

so that it can be denoted by N(λ, λ).

(Remember that, for a Poisson distribution, mean = variance.)

For values of λ larger than 10 the Poisson probability graph becomes less positively skewed and more bell-shaped in appearance thus making the Normal approximation appropriate. Figure 2.21 shows the Poisson probability graph for the two cases $\lambda = 3$ and $\lambda = 25$. You will see that for $\lambda = 3$ the graph is positively skewed but for $\lambda = 25$ it is approximately bell-shaped.

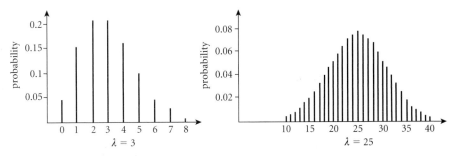

Figure 2.21

EXAMPLE 2.5

The annual number of deaths nationally from a rare disease, X, may be modelled by the Poisson distribution with mean 25. One year there are 31 deaths and it is suggested that the disease is on the increase.

What is the probability of 31 or more deaths in a year, assuming the mean has remained at 25?

SOLUTION

The Poisson distribution with mean 25 may be approximated by the Normal distribution with parameters

Mean: 25

Standard deviation: $\sqrt{25} = 5$

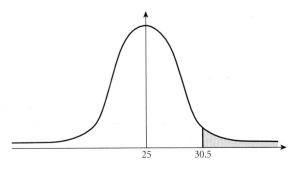

Figure 2.22

The probability of there being 31 or more deaths in a year, $P(X \geqslant 31)$, is given by $1 - \Phi(z)$, where

$$z = \frac{30.5 - 25}{5} = 1.1.$$

(Note the continuity correction, replacing 31 by 30.5.)

The required area is $1 - \Phi(1.1)$

$$= 1 - 0.8643$$
$$= 0.1357$$

This is not a particularly low probability; it is quite likely that there would be that many deaths in any one year.

EXERCISE 2B

1   The intelligence of an individual is frequently described by a positive integer known as an IQ (intelligence quotient). The distribution of IQs amongst children of a certain age-group can be approximated by a Normal probability model with mean 100 and standard deviation 15. Write a sentence stating what you understand about the age-group from the fact that $\Phi(2.5) = 0.994$.

A class of 30 children is selected at random from the age-group. Calculate (to 3 significant figures) the probability that at least one member of the class has an IQ of 138 or more.

[SMP]

2   A certain examination has a mean mark of 100 and a standard deviation of 15. The marks can be assumed to be Normally distributed.
    (i)   What is the least mark needed to be in the top 35% of students taking this examination?
    (ii) Between which two marks will the middle 90% of the students lie?
    (iii) 150 students take this examination. Calculate the number of students likely to score 110 or over.

[MEI]

3   25% of Flapper Fish have red spots, the rest have blue spots. A fisherman nets 10 Flapper Fish. What are the probabilities that
    (i)   exactly 8 have blue spots
    (ii) at least 8 have blue spots?

A large number of samples, each of 100 Flapper Fish, are taken.
    (iii) What is
        (a) the mean?   (b) the standard deviation
        of the number of red-spotted fish per sample?
    (iv) What is the probability of a sample of 100 Flapper Fish containing over 30 with red spots?

4 A fair coin is tossed 10 times. Evaluate the probability that exactly half of the tosses result in heads.

The same coin is tossed 100 times. Use the Normal approximation to the binomial to estimate the probability that exactly half of the tosses result in heads. Also estimate the probability that more than 60 of the tosses result in heads.

Explain why a continuity correction is made when using the Normal approximation to the binomial and the reason for the adoption of this correction.

[MEI]

5 State conditions under which a binomial probability model can be well approximated by a Normal model.

X is a random variable with the distribution B(12, 0.42).

(i) Anne uses the binomial distribution to calculate the probability that $X < 4$ and gives 4 significant figures in her answer. What answer should she get?

(ii) Ben uses a Normal distribution to calculate an approximation for the probability that $X < 4$ and gives 4 significant figures in his answer. What answer should he get?

(iii) Given that Ben's working is correct, calculate the percentage error in his answer.

[Cambridge]

6 During an advertising campaign, the manufacturers of Wolfitt (a dog food) claimed that 60% of dog owners preferred to buy Wolfitt.

(i) Assuming that the manufacturer's claim is correct for the population of dog owners, calculate

(a) using the binomial distribution

(b) using a Normal approximation to the binomial

the probability that at least 6 of a random sample of 8 dog owners prefer to buy Wolfitt. Comment on the agreement, or disagreement, between your two values. Would the agreement be better or worse if the proportion had been 80% instead of 60%?

(ii) Continuing to assume that the manufacturer's figure of 60% is correct, use the Normal approximation to the binomial to estimate the probability that, of a random sample of 100 dog owners, the number preferring to buy Wolfitt is between 60 and 70 inclusive.

[MEI]

7 A multiple-choice examination consists of 20 questions, for each of which the candidate is required to tick as correct one of three possible answers. Exactly one answer to each question is correct. A correct answer gets 1 mark and a wrong answer gets 0 marks. Consider a candidate who has complete ignorance about every question and therefore ticks at random. What is the probability that he gets a particular answer correct? Calculate the mean and variance of the number of questions he answers correctly.

The examiners wish to ensure that no more than 1% of completely ignorant candidates pass the examination. Use the Normal approximation to the binomial, working throughout to 3 decimal places, to establish the pass mark that meets this requirement.

[MEI]

8 A large box contains many plastic syringes, but previous experience indicates that 10% of the syringes in the box are defective. Five syringes are taken at random from the box. Use a binomial model to calculate, giving your answers correct to 3 decimal places, the probability that
(i) none of the five syringes is defective
(ii) at least two syringes out of the five are defective.

Discuss the validity of the binomial model in this context.

Instead of removing five syringes, 100 syringes are picked at random and removed. A Normal distribution may be used to estimate the probability that at least 15 out of the 100 syringes are defective. Give a reason why it may be convenient to use a Normal distribution to do this, and calculate the required estimate.

[Cambridge]

9 A telephone exchange serves 2000 subscribers, and at any moment during the busiest period there is a probability of $\frac{1}{30}$ for each subscriber that he will require a line. Assuming that the needs of subscribers are independent, write down an expression for the probability that exactly N lines will be occupied at any moment during the busiest period.

Use the Normal distribution to estimate the minimum number of lines that would ensure that the probability that a call cannot be made because all the lines are occupied is less than 0.01.

Investigate whether the total number of lines needed would be reduced if the subscribers were split into two groups of 1000, each with its own set of lines.

[MEI]

10 A drug manufacturer claims that a certain drug cures a blood disease on average 80% of the time. To check the claim, an independent tester uses the drug on a random sample of *n* patients. He decides to accept the claim if *k* or more patients are cured.

Assume that the manufacturer's claim is true.

(i) State the distribution of *X*, the number of patients cured. Find the probability that the claim will be accepted when 15 individuals are tested and *k* is set at 10.

A more extensive trial is now undertaken on a random sample of 100 patients.

(ii) State a suitable approximating distribution for *X*, and so estimate the probability that the claim will be rejected if *k* is set at 75.

(iii) Find the largest value of *k* such that the probability of the claim being rejected is no more than 1%.

[MEI]

11 The number of cars per minute entering a multi-storey car park can be modelled by a Poisson distribution with mean 2. What is the probability that three cars enter during a period of one minute?

What are the mean and the standard deviation of the number of cars entering the car park during a period of 30 minutes? Use the Normal approximation to the Poisson distribution to estimate the probability that at least 50 cars enter in any one 30-minute period.

[MEI]

12 State the mean and variance of the Poisson distribution. State under what circumstances the Normal distribution can be used as an approximation to the Poisson distribution.

Readings, on a counter, of the number of particles emitted from a radioactive source in a time *T* seconds have a Poisson distribution with mean $250T$. A ten-second count is made. Find the probabilities of readings of

(i) more than 2600   **(ii)** 2400 or more.

[JMB]

13 A large computer system which is in constant operation requires an average of 30 service calls per year.

(i) State the average number of service calls per month, taking a month to be $\frac{1}{12}$ of a year. What assumptions need to be made for the Poisson distribution to be used to model the number of calls in a given month?

(ii) Use the Poisson distribution to find the probability that at least one service call is required in January. Obtain the probability that there is at least one service call in each month of the year.

(iii) The service contract offers a discount if the number of service calls in the year is 24 or fewer. Use a suitable approximating distribution to find the probability of obtaining the discount in any particular year.

[MEI]

14 The number of night calls to a fire station in a small town can be modelled by a Poisson distribution with a mean of 4.2 per night.

Use the Normal approximation to the Poisson distribution to estimate the probability that in any particular week (Sunday to Saturday inclusive) the number of night calls to the fire station will be

(i) at least 30

(ii) exactly 30

(iii) between 25 and 35 inclusive.

15 At a busy intersection of roads, accidents requiring the summoning of an ambulance occur with a frequency, on average, of 1.8 per week. These accidents occur randomly, so that it may be assumed that they follow a Poisson distribution.

Use a suitable approximating distribution to find the probability that in any particular year (of 52 weeks) the number of accidents at the intersection will be

(i) at most 100

(ii) exactly 100

(iii) between 95 and 105 inclusive.

16 Tina is a traffic warden. The number of parking tickets she issues per day, from Monday to Saturday inclusive, may be modelled by a Poisson distribution with mean 11.5.

(i) Find the probability that on a particular Tuesday she issues at least 15 parking tickets.

(ii) Find the probability that during any week (excluding Sunday) she issues at least 50 parking tickets.

(iii) Find the probability that during four consecutive weeks she issues

  (a) at least 50 parking tickets each week

  (b) at least 200 parking tickets altogether.

  Account for the difference in the two answers.

17 The number of emails I receive per day on my computer may be modelled by a Poisson distribution with mean 8.5.

(i) Use the most appropriate method to calculate the probability that I receive

  (a) at least 8 emails tomorrow

  (b) at least 240 emails next June

  (c) at least 2920 emails next year.

(ii) What assumptions do you have to make to find the probabilities in parts **(i) (b)** and **(c)**?

(iii) Compare your answers to parts **(i) (a)**, **(b)** and **(c)** and account for the variation.

18 The random variable $X \sim \mathrm{B}(n, 0.02)$.

  (i) Write down an appropriate approximating distribution for
    (a) $n = 500$
    (b) $n = 5000$.

  In the remainder of the question take $n = 5000$.

  (ii) Use both the original distribution and its approximating distribution to calculate $\mathrm{P}(X = 95)$. Compare your methods and your answers.

  (iii) Find $\mathrm{P}(95 < X < 105)$.

  (iv) Find values of a and b such that $\mathrm{P}(a < X < b) = 0.99$.

1 One spring, a grower of Christmas trees planted a large number of seedlings. Some years later, just before Christmas, he measured the heights of a random sample of the trees. He found that 16% had a height of over 2.6 m and 25% had a height of less than 1.7 m. His observations also suggested that the distribution of heights is Normal.

  (i) Illustrate the information by a sketch.

  (ii) By solving a pair of simultaneous equations, obtain estimates of the mean and standard deviation of heights. Explain why it is not possible to calculate exact values for the mean and standard deviation of the population from the information given.

  (iii) The grower estimates that there are about 5000 trees in the plantation, and he decides to sell all those with heights of 2 m or more. Estimate the number of trees he has to sell.

[MEI]

2 The quantity of milk in bottles from a dairy is Normally distributed with mean 1.036 pints and standard deviation 0.014 pints.

  (i) Show that the probability of a randomly chosen bottle containing less than a pint is very nearly 0.5%.

  In the rest of this question take the answer 0.5% to be exact.

  (ii) A crate contains 24 bottles. Find the probability that
    (a) no bottles contain less than a pint of milk
    (b) at most 1 bottle contains less than a pint of milk.

  A milk float is loaded with 150 crates (3600 bottles) of milk.

  (iii) State the expected number of bottles containing less than a pint of milk.

  (iv) Give a suitable approximating distribution for the number of bottles containing less than a pint of milk. Use this distribution to find the probability that more than 20 bottles contain less than a pint of milk.

[MEI]

3 A certain type of light bulb has a lifetime which is Normally distributed with mean 1100 hours and standard deviation 80 hours.

(i) Find the probability that a randomly chosen bulb will last at least 1000 hours.

(ii) Find the lifetime which is exceeded by 95% of bulbs.

A newly installed light fitting takes six of these bulbs. The lifetimes of the bulbs are independent of one another.

(iii) Show that the probability that the light fitting can run for 1000 hours without any of the bulbs failing is a little over 0.5.

(iv) The probability that the light fitting can run for t hours without any of the bulbs failing is 0.95. Find t.

[MEI]

4 A survey conducted by a local education authority requires schools to complete a questionnaire about a sample of their students. The sample is defined as all students born on the 5th of any month, so the probability of a randomly chosen student being in the sample is $\frac{12}{365}$, or about 0.0329.

The A level year in a secondary school consists of 100 students.

(i) Find the probability that none of these students appears in the sample.

The school has 1500 students in total.

(ii) Write down the expectation and the standard deviation of the total number of students sampled in a school of this size.

(iii) Use a suitable approximating distribution to find the probability that the number of students sampled is more than 60.

(iv) Find the greatest value of k such that it is 95% certain that k or more students will be sampled.

(v) What should the local authority's reaction be if the school returns information about just 32 students?

[MEI]

5 Eggs are graded according to length L mm. A size 3 egg is one for which $60 < L < 65$. An egg producer finds that 37% of her eggs are larger than size 3 while 21% are smaller. Assume that L is Normally distributed with mean μ and standard deviation σ.

(i) Show the information given on a sketch of the distribution of L.

(ii) Write down two equations involving μ and σ and solve them.

Further investigation shows that
(A) $L > 70$ for about 7% of eggs, and
(B) $L < 55$ for less than 1% of eggs.

(iii) Determine whether (A) is consistent with the distribution found in part **(ii)**.

(iv) Determine whether (B) is consistent with the distribution found in part **(ii)**.

[MEI]

6 A test consists of 100 multiple choice questions, each having four possible answers labelled *A*, *B*, *C*, *D*.

Anna does not know the answers to any of the questions so she guesses at random.
- **(i)** Find the probability that
  - **(a)** she gets none of the first 10 answers right
  - **(b)** she gets 4 or more of the first 10 answers right.
- **(ii)** Using a suitable approximating distribution, find the probability that Anna gets exactly 25 answers correct on the whole paper.
- **(iii)** The pass mark on the paper is 40. Show that Anna is extremely unlikely to pass.
- **(iv)** Bella knows the correct answers to 25 questions but guesses at the rest. Obtain Bella's expected score and explain carefully whether or not she is likely to pass.

[MEI]

7 In Britain the average number of babies born per day is currently about 2040.

- **(i)** Explain briefly why the distribution of the numbers of births might well be modelled by the Poisson distribution. Write down the mean and standard deviation of a suitable approximating Normal distribution.
- **(ii)** Calculate the probability that on a randomly chosen day the number of babies born is less than 2000.
- **(iii)** Obtain values *a* and *b* such that the number of babies born on a randomly chosen day is 95% certain to lie between *a* and *b*.
- **(iv)** Obtain a value *c* which is a reasonable upper limit for the number of babies born in Britain in a year.

[MEI]

8 At a play centre parents pay a fixed fee and may leave their children for as long as they wish. The management's records show that the most common length of stay is 80 minutes, and that 25% of children stay longer than 90 minutes. The length of time a child stays appears to be reasonably well modelled by a Normal distribution.

- **(i)** Show the information given on a sketch of the Normal distribution. Determine the mean and standard deviation of the distribution.

In the rest of the question assume that the distribution is $N(80, 15^2)$.
- **(ii)** Calculate the probability that a child stays more than 2 hours.

The management decide to introduce a closing time of 5.00 pm.
- **(iii)** Explain why the proposed model could not now apply to children arriving at 4.00 pm.
- **(iv)** Give a latest time of arrival for which you consider the model still to be reasonable. Justify your answer.

[MEI]

9 An angler goes fishing at the same spot every Saturday morning. From long experience he reckons that the number of fish he catches per hour can be modelled by the Poisson distribution with mean 3.2. One particular Saturday he fishes for two hours.

(i) Find the following probabilities, giving your answers correct to 4 decimal places
   (a) he catches exactly three fish in the first hour
   (b) he catches three or more fish in the second hour
   (c) he catches six or more fish in the two hours.

(ii) Find the probability that he catches three fish in the first hour and three or more fish in the second hour.

The angler counts the number of fish he catches over a total of 40 hours.

(iii) Write down a suitable approximating distribution for the number of fish caught, and find the probability that this number is at least 100.

(iv) If in fact the angler caught fewer than 100 fish in 40 hours, what would this suggest about the model, and why?

[MEI]

10 Electronic sensors of a certain type fail when they become too hot. The temperature at which a randomly chosen sensor fails is $T\,°C$, where T is modelled as a Normal random variable with mean μ and standard deviation σ.

In a laboratory test, 98% of a random sample of sensors continued working at a temperature of $80\,°C$, but only 4% continued working at $104\,°C$.

(i) Show the given information on a sketch of the distribution of T.

(ii) Determine estimates of the values of μ and σ.

More extensive tests confirm that T is Normally distributed, but with $\mu = 94.5$ and $\sigma = 5.7$. Use these figures in the rest of the question.

(iii) Determine what proportion of sensors will operate in boiling water (i.e. at $100\,°C$).

(iv) The manufacturers wish to quote a safe operating temperature at which 99% of the sensors will work. What temperature should they quote?

[MEI]

11 In a reading test for eight-year-old children, it is found that a reading score X is Normally distributed with mean 5.0 and standard deviation 2.0.

(i) What proportion of children would you expect to score between 4.5 and 6.0?

(ii) There are about 700 000 eight-year-olds in the country. How many would you expect to have a reading score of more than twice the mean?

(iii) Why might educationalists refer to the reading score X as a 'score out of 10'?

The reading score is often reported, after scaling, as a value Y which is Normally distributed, with mean 100 and standard deviation 15. Values of Y are usually given to the nearest integer.

(iv) Find the probability that a randomly chosen eight-year-old gets a score, after scaling, of 103.

(v) What range of Y scores would you expect to be attained by the best 20% of readers?

[MEI]

12 The speeds of a large random sample of cars, travelling along a certain stretch of road, were recorded. It was found that 10% of the cars observed were exceeding the speed limit of 70 mph and that 50% were travelling at speeds under 56 mph. Assume that the speeds, V, of all the cars on the road are Normally distributed with mean μ and standard deviation σ.

(i) Show the given information on a sketch of the distribution of V.

(ii) State an estimate of the value of μ and find an estimate for σ. Explain why your values are only estimates.

(iii) Estimate the percentage of cars travelling faster than 50 mph.

(iv) Estimate a symmetrical range of speeds within which 99% of the cars were travelling.

(v) Comment on the assumption of Normality when describing the distribution of speeds of cars.

[MEI]

13 An apple grower classifies his apples by mass, x grams, as small, medium or large as follows.

Small	Medium	Large
$x < 90$	$90 \leqslant x < 120$	$120 \leqslant x$

Assume that the masses are Normally distributed with mean μ grams and standard deviation σ grams. In a large crop of apples it was found that 9% were small and 25% were large.

(i) Show this information on a sketch.

(ii) Form two equations in μ and σ. Use them to calculate values for the mean and standard deviation of the masses of the apples, giving your answers correct to 2 decimal places.

When rounded to the nearest integer, $\mu = 110$ and $\sigma = 15$. Use these values in the remainder of the question.

(iii) Two apples are chosen at random, from the crop. Find the probability that at least one of them has a mass of 100 grams or more.

(iv) Find the median mass of a medium size apple.

[MEI]

14 A company markets cylinders of butane gas in liquid form. The nominal content of a cylinder is 15 kg.

The process which is used to fill the cylinders is subject to slight variation. Contents of cylinders are in fact Normally distributed with mean $\mu = 15.4$ and standard deviation $\sigma = 0.25$, both measured in kilograms.

(i) Find the proportion of cylinders which contain less than 15 kg.

(ii) It is found that 99% of cylinders contain less than L kg of butane. Find the value of L.

An inspector tests the mass of butane in a sample of ten cylinders, chosen at random from a large batch. He decides to reject the batch if two or more cylinders in the sample contain less than 15 kg, otherwise he accepts the batch.

(iii) What is the probability that he will accept the batch?

The company needs to be 95% sure that the batch will be accepted. A mathematician advises them that to achieve this the probability of a cylinder containing less than 15 kg must be reduced to 0.0368.

(iv) This can be done by changing μ. Find the appropriate new value of μ.

(v) Suggest, without further calculation, how else a probability of 0.0368 could be achieved.

[MEI]

15 In a certain constituency, 35% of the votes at the last General Election went to the Liberal Democrats, and the rest to the other political parties. A year later, a random sample of people from the constituency is asked how they would vote now. Assume that the support for the Liberal Democrats across the whole constituency has not changed since the General Election.

(i) For a sample of size n, state the distribution of X, the number of people in the sample who would vote Liberal Democrat.

(ii) For a sample of 20 voters, find the probability that at least 5 would vote Liberal Democrat.

(iii) For a sample of 100 voters, use a suitable approximating distribution to find the probability that between 30 and 40 people, inclusive, would vote Liberal Democrat.

(iv) For a sample of 1000 voters, find integers a and b such that the number who say they would vote Liberal Democrat is approximately 99% certain to be between a and b.

(v) For a sample of 1000 voters, suppose that 400 said they would vote Liberal Democrat. What light would this shed on the parameter of the distribution proposed in part **(i)**?

[MEI]

16 Anna travels to college every day by bus. The bus is due to leave at 0825. You may assume that the journey times are Normally distributed with mean 27 minutes and standard deviation 4 minutes.

For parts **(i)** to **(iii)** you may assume that the bus leaves on time.
(i) Find the probability that Anna arrives at college between 0850 and 0855.
(ii) By what time does Anna arrive on 90% of days?

Anna needs to be at college by 0900 each day.
(iii) Find the probability that Anna is late
     (a) on any one day   **(b)** at most once in a five-day week.
(iv) How late can the bus leave so that there is at least a 75% chance that Anna arrives at college by 0900?

[MEI]

17 A medical student suspects that the (systolic) blood pressure of university students is Normally distributed with mean μ and standard deviation σ. A large random sample of such students had their blood pressures taken. Some statistics for the data collected are as follows.

Least value in the data:	92.5
Lower quartile (25th percentile):	110.6
Median:	118.0
Upper quartile (75th percentile):	125.4
Greatest value in the data:	140.7

(i) Identify one feature of the statistics which supports the suggestion that the blood pressures of university students follow a Normal distribution.
(ii) Show the given information on a sketch of the Normal curve.
(iii) State an estimate for μ and use the upper quartile to show that $\sigma \approx 11$.

In the rest of this question use your estimated value for μ and the value 11 for σ.
(iv) Find the probability that a student chosen at random has a blood pressure between 110 and 120.
(v) How large a random sample is needed to be 99% sure of finding at least one student with a blood pressure lower than 110?

[MEI]

18 Scores on an IQ test are modelled by the Normal distribution with mean 100 and standard deviation 15. The scores are reported to the nearest integer.

(i) Find the probability that a person chosen at random scores
     (a) exactly 105   **(b)** more than 110.
(ii) Only people with IQs in the top 2.5% are admitted to the organisation *BRAIN*. What is the minimum score for admission?
(iii) Find the probability that, in a random sample of 20 people, exactly 6 score more than 110.
(iv) Find the probability that, in a random sample of 200 people, at least 60 score more than 110.

[MEI]

19 *Extralite* are testing a new long-life bulb. The lifetimes, in hours, are assumed to be Normally distributed with mean μ and standard deviation σ. After extensive tests, they find that 19% of bulbs have a lifetime exceeding 5000 hours, while 5% have a lifetime under 4000 hours.

 (i) Illustrate this information on a sketch.
 (ii) Show that $\sigma = 396$ and find the value of μ.

In the remainder of this question take μ to be 4650 and σ to be 400.
 (iii) Find the probability that a bulb chosen at random has a lifetime between 4250 and 4750 hours.
 (iv) *Extralite* wish to quote a lifetime which will be exceeded by 99% of bulbs. What time, correct to the nearest 100 hours, should they quote?

A new school classroom has six light-fittings, each fitted with an *Extralite* long-life bulb.
 (v) Find the probability that no more than one bulb needs to be replaced within the first 4250 hours of use.

[MEI]

20 A supermarket takes delivery of bags of potatoes with nominal weight 5 kg. A large number of such bags are weighed with the result that the mean weight is 5.5 kg and 10% of the bags are below nominal weight. You may assume that the weights, X kg, of bags of potatoes are modelled by the Normal distribution $N(\mu, \sigma^2)$.

 (i) Illustrate the information on a diagram and show that an estimate of the standard deviation is about 0.4 kg.
 (ii) Taking $\mu = 5.5$ and $\sigma = 0.4$, find the probability that a bag chosen at random weighs between 5.3 kg and 5.8 kg.
 (iii) Assuming the mean remains the same, find the required standard deviation in order that at most 2% of bags are below nominal weight.
 (iv) A customer chooses two of the original bags at random. You may assume that the total weight is modelled by the Normal distribution $N(2\mu, 2\sigma^2)$, where $\mu = 5.5$ and $\sigma = 0.4$. Find the probability that she gets a total weight of at least 10 kg of potatoes.

[MEI]

1 The Normal distribution with mean μ and standard deviation σ is denoted by $N(\mu, \sigma^2)$.

2 This may be given in standardised form by using the transformation

$$z = \frac{x - \mu}{\sigma}.$$

3 In the standardised form, $N(0, 1)$, the mean is 0, the standard deviation and variance both 1.

4 The standardised Normal curve is given by

$$\phi(z) = \frac{1}{\sqrt{2\pi}} \, e^{-\frac{1}{2}z^2}$$

5 The area to the left of the value z in the diagram below, representing the probability of a value less than z, is denoted by $\Phi(z)$ and is read from tables.

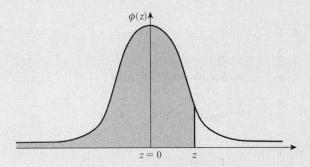

6 The Normal distribution may be used to approximate suitable discrete distributions but continuity corrections are then required.

7 The binomial distribution $B(n, p)$ may be approximated by $N(np, npq)$, provided n is large and p is not close to 0 or 1.

8 The Poisson distribution Poisson (λ) may be approximated by $N(\lambda, \lambda)$, provided λ is about 10 or more.

3

Samples and hypothesis testing

When we spend money on testing an item, we are buying confidence in its performance.

Tony Cutler

Interpreting sample data using the Normal distribution

THE AVONFORD STAR

Avonford set to become greenhouse?

From our Science Correspondent Ama Williams

On a recent visit to Avonford Community College, I was intrigued to find experiments being conducted to measure the level of carbon dioxide in the air we are all breathing. Readers will of course know that high levels of carbon dioxide are associated with the greenhouse effect.

Lecturer Ray Sharp showed me round his laboratory. 'It is delicate work, measuring parts per million, but I am trying to establish what is the normal level in this area. Yesterday we took ten readings and you can see the results for yourself: 336, 334, 332, 332, 331, 331, 330, 330, 328, 326.'

When I commented that there seemed to be a lot of variation between the readings, Ray assured me that that was quite in order.

'I have taken hundreds of these measurements in the past,' he said. 'There is always a standard deviation of 2.5. That's just natural variation.'

I suggested to Ray that his students should test whether these results are significantly above the accepted value of 328 parts per million. Certainly they made me feel uneasy. Is the greenhouse effect starting here in Avonford?

Ray Sharp has been trying to establish the carbon dioxide level at Avonford. How do you interpret his figures? Do you think the correspondent has a point when she says she is worried that the greenhouse effect is already happening in Avonford?

If suitable sampling procedures have not been used, then the resulting data may be worthless, indeed positively misleading. You may wonder if that is the case with Ray's figures, and about the accuracy of his analysis of the samples too. His data are used in subsequent working in this chapter, but you may well feel there is something of a question mark hanging over them. You should always be prepared to treat data with a healthy degree of caution.

Putting aside any concerns about the quality of the data, what conclusions can you draw from them?

Estimating the population mean, μ

Ray Sharp's data were as follows.

$$336, 334, 332, 332, 331, 331, 330, 330, 328, 326$$

His intention in collecting them was to estimate the mean of the parent population, the population mean.

The mean of these figures, the sample mean, is given by

$$\bar{x} = \frac{(336 + 334 + 332 + 332 + 331 + 331 + 330 + 330 + 328 + 326)}{10}$$

$$= 331.$$

What does this tell you about the population mean, μ?

It tells you that it is about 331 but it certainly does not tell you that it is definitely and exactly 331. If Ray took another sample, its mean would probably not be 331 but you would be surprised (and suspicious) if it were very far away from it. If he took lots of samples, all of size 10, you would expect their means to be close together but certainly not all the same.

If you took 1000 such samples, each of size 10, the distribution of their means might look like figure 3.1.

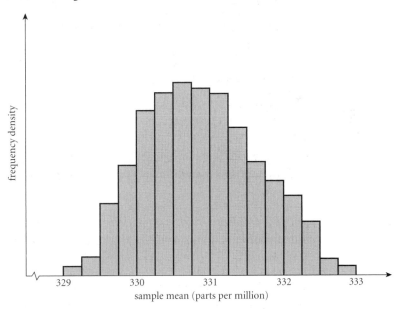

Figure 3.1

You will notice that this distribution looks rather like the Normal distribution and so may well wonder if this is indeed the case.

The distribution of sample means

In this chapter, it is assumed that the underlying population has a Normal distribution with mean μ and standard deviation σ; so it can be denoted by $N(\mu, \sigma^2)$. In that case the distribution of the means of samples is indeed Normal; its mean is μ and its standard deviation is $\dfrac{\sigma}{\sqrt{n}}$. This is called the *sampling distribution of the means*, or often just the *sampling distribution*, and is denoted by $N\left(\mu, \dfrac{\sigma^2}{n}\right)$. This is illustrated in figure 3.2

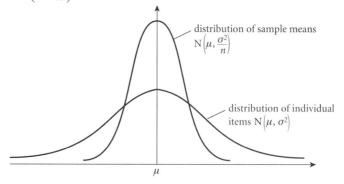

Figure 3.2

e *Looking at the sampling distribution*

The following example illustrates how the expression $\dfrac{\sigma}{\sqrt{n}}$ arises. In part **(i)** it involves the distribution of a random variable formed by summing several Normal random variables. This is not difficult but it may well be unfamiliar to you.

EXAMPLE 3.1

A company sells tins of sardines. The weights of the sardines are Normally distributed with mean 30 g and standard deviation 5 g. Each tin contains four randomly selected sardines. Describe

(i) the distribution of the total weight of fish in a tin

(ii) the distribution of the mean weights of the sardines in a tin.

SOLUTION

(i) For the individual fish, $\mu = 30$, $\sigma = 5$, variance $= \sigma^2 = 25$.

The sardines in a tin may be regarded as a random sample with size $n = 4$.

The total weight is the sum of four Normal variables, one for each sardine. So the distribution of the total weight is also Normal; its mean and variance are the sums of the means and variances for the individual sardines, as shown opposite.

	Sardine 1		Sardine 2		Sardine 3		Sardine 4		Total
Mean	30	+	30	+	30	+	30	=	120
Variance	25	+	25	+	25	+	25	=	100

So the distribution of the total weight is Normal, with mean 120 g, variance 100 g and standard deviation $\sqrt{100} = 10$ g.

(ii) From this it follows that the distribution of the mean weights of the sardines in a tin is also Normal.

Its mean is $\dfrac{120}{4} = 30$ g and its standard deviation is $\dfrac{10}{4} = 2.5$ g.

? Is the answer to part **(ii)** consistent with the sampling distribution $N\left(\mu, \dfrac{\sigma^2}{n}\right)$?

The result for the sampling distribution is a special case of the Central Limit Theorem which is covered in *Statistics 3*. This theorem deals with cases when the distribution of the underlying population is not necessarily Normal.

A hypothesis test for the mean using the Normal distribution

If your intention in collecting sample data is to test a theory, then you should set up a hypothesis test.

Ray Sharp was mainly interested in establishing data on carbon dioxide levels for Avonford. The correspondent, however, wanted to know whether levels were above normal, and so she could have set up and conducted a test.

Here is the relevant information, given in a more condensed format.

EXAMPLE 3.2

Ama Williams believes that the carbon dioxide level in Avonford has risen above the usual level of 328 parts per million. A sample of 10 specimens of Avonford air are collected and the carbon dioxide level within them is determined. The results are as follows.

336, 334, 332, 332, 331, 331, 330, 330, 328, 326.

Extensive previous research has shown that the standard deviation of the levels within such samples is 2.5, and that the distribution may be assumed to be Normal.

Use these data to test, at the 0.1% significance level, Ama's belief that the level of carbon dioxide at Avonford is above normal.

SOLUTION

As usual with hypothesis tests, you use the distribution of the statistic you are measuring, in this case the Normal distribution of the sample means, to decide which values of the test statistic are sufficiently extreme as to suggest that the alternative hypothesis, not the null hypothesis, is true.

Null hypothesis, H_0: $\quad\quad\quad \mu = 328 \quad\quad$ The level of carbon dioxide at Avonford is normal.

Alternative hypothesis, H_1: $\quad \mu > 328 \quad\quad$ The level of carbon dioxide at Avonford is above normal.

One-tail test at the 0.1% significance level.

Method 1: Using critical regions

Since the distribution of sample means is $N\left(\mu, \dfrac{\sigma^2}{n}\right)$, critical values for a test on

the sample mean are given by $\mu \pm k \times \dfrac{\sigma}{\sqrt{n}}$.

In this case, if H_0 is true, $\mu = 328$; $\sigma = 2.5$; $n = 10$.

The test is one-tail, for $\mu > 328$, so only the right-hand tail applies. This gives a value of $k = 3.09$ since Normal distribution tables give $\Phi(3.09) = 0.999$ and so $1 - \Phi(3.09) = 0.001$.

The critical value is thus $328 + 3.09 \times \dfrac{2.5}{\sqrt{10}} = 330.4$, as shown in figure 3.3.

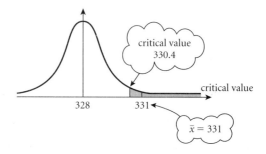

Figure 3.3

However, the sample mean $\bar{x} = 331$, and $331 > 330.4$.

Therefore the sample mean lies within the critical region, and so the null hypothesis is rejected in favour of the alternative hypothesis: that the mean carbon dioxide level is above 328, at the 0.1% significance level.

Method 2: Using probabilities

The distribution of sample means, $\overline{X}$, is $N\left(\mu, \dfrac{\sigma^2}{n}\right)$.

According to the null hypothesis, $\mu = 328$ and it is known that $\sigma = 2.5$ and $n = 10$.

So this distribution is $N\left(328, \dfrac{2.5^2}{10}\right)$; see figure 3.4.

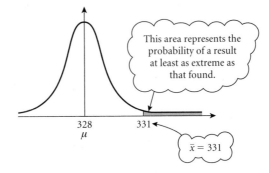

Figure 3.4

The probability of the mean, $\overline{X}$, of a randomly chosen sample being greater than the value found, i.e. 331, is given by

$$P(\overline{X} \geqslant 331) = 1 - \Phi\left(\frac{331 - 328}{\dfrac{2.5}{\sqrt{10}}}\right)$$

$$= 1 - \Phi(3.79) = 1 - 0.999\,93 = 0.000\,07$$

Since $0.000\,07 < 0.001$, the required significance level (0.1%), the null hypothesis is rejected in favour of the alternative hypothesis.

Method 3: Using critical ratios

The *critical ratio* is given by

$$z = \frac{\text{observed value} - \text{expected value}}{\text{standard deviation}}$$

In this case

$$z = \frac{331 - 328}{\dfrac{2.5}{\sqrt{10}}} = 3.79$$

This is now compared with the critical value for z, in this case $z = 3.09$. Since $3.79 > 3.09$, H_0 is rejected.

Notes

1 A hypothesis test should be formulated before the data are collected and not after. If sample data lead you to form a hypothesis, then you should plan a suitable test and collect further data on which to conduct it. It is not clear whether or not the test in the previous example was being carried out on the same data which were used to formulate the hypothesis.

2 If the data were not collected properly, any test carried out on them may be worthless.

Known and estimated standard deviation

Notice that you can only use this method of hypothesis testing if you already know the value of the standard deviation of the parent population, σ. Ray Sharp had said that from taking hundreds of measurements he knew it to be 2.5.

It is more often the situation that you do not know the population standard deviation or variance, and have to estimate it from your sample data. Provided the sample size, n, is sufficiently large – at least 50 as a rule of thumb, but the larger the better – the sample standard deviation may be used as an estimate of the population standard deviation. Theoretically, it can be shown that the sample variance, s^2, is an unbiased estimate of the population variance, σ^2. This approximation is used in the following example.

EXAMPLE 3.3

An IQ test, established some years ago, was designed to have a mean score of 100. A researcher puts forward a theory that people are becoming more intelligent (as measured by this particular test). She selects a random sample of 150 people, all of whom take the test. The results of the tests, where x represents the score obtained, are as follows.

$$n = 150, \qquad \Sigma x = 15\,483, \qquad \Sigma x^2 = 1\,631\,680$$

Carry out a suitable hypothesis test on the researcher's theory, at the 1% significance level. You may assume that the test scores are Normally distributed.

SOLUTION

H_0: The parent population mean is unchanged, i.e. $\mu = 100$.
H_1: The parent population mean has increased, i.e. $\mu > 100$.

From the sample summary statistics, the mean and standard deviation are as follows.

$$\bar{x} = \frac{\Sigma x}{n} = \frac{15\,483}{150} = 103.22$$

$$s = \sqrt{\frac{\Sigma x^2 - n\bar{x}^2}{n-1}} = \sqrt{\frac{1\,631\,680 - 150 \times 103.22^2}{149}}$$
$$= 15.0 \text{ (to 3 s.f.)}$$

The standardised z value corresponding to $\bar{x} = 103.22$ is calculated using $\mu = 100$ and approximating σ by $s = 15.0$.

$$z = \frac{\bar{x} - \mu_0}{\dfrac{\sigma}{\sqrt{n}}} = \frac{103.22 - 100}{\dfrac{15}{\sqrt{150}}} = 2.629$$

For the 1% significance level, the critical value is $z = 2.326$.
The test statistic is compared with the critical value and since $2.629 > 2.326$ the null hypothesis is rejected.

The evidence supports the view that scores on this IQ test are now higher; see figure 3.5.

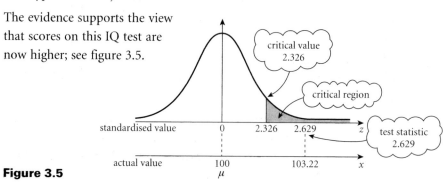

Figure 3.5

Using a graphic calculator

It is fairly easy to set up a graphic calculator to carry out a Normal z test, displaying both the results and the associated area under the Normal curve.

The null hypothesis is given by $H_0: \mu = \mu_0$.

You need to enter values for
- the population mean under test, μ_0
- the known (or estimated) population standard deviation, σ
- the sample mean, $\bar{x}$
- the sample size, n.

Finally choose the form of the alternative hypothesis H_1 by highlighting one of the three options.

$$\neq \mu_0 \text{ (two-tail test) or } < \mu_0 \text{ or } > \mu_0 \text{ (one-tail test)}$$

Figure 3.6 shows the output for Example 3.3 obtained by carrying out the following steps.

1 Enter the required information on the screen.

Population mean to test using $H_0: \mu = 100$	$\mu_0 = 100$
Standard deviation	$\sigma = 15$
Sample mean	$\bar{x} = 103.22$
Sample size	$n = 150$
Alternative hypothesis $H_1: \mu > 100$	$> \mu_0$

2 Display the results of the z test.

Test statistic (standardised $\bar{x}$ value)	$z = 2.629\ldots$
$P(Z > 2.629\ldots)$	$p = 0.004\,28$
Sample mean	$\bar{x} = 103.22$
Sample size	$n = 150$

3 Display graphically the test statistic, z, and $P(Z > 2.629\ldots)$, p, with the associated area shaded.

Step 1

Step 2

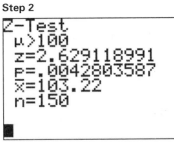

Step 3

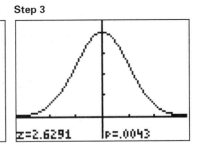

Figure 3.6

You can see from figure 3.6 that, at the 1% significance level, the null hypothesis is rejected in favour of the alternative hypothesis, $H_1: \mu > 100$, since $2.629\ldots > 2.326$ (the critical value) or because $P(Z > 2.629\ldots) = 0.004\,28\ldots$, which is less than 0.05.

Note

The illustrations on the previous page are taken from a TI-83 graphic calculator. Similar screen shots are possible from other graphic calculators.

1 For each of the following, the random variable $X \sim N(\mu, \sigma^2)$, with *known* standard deviation. A random sample of size n is taken from the parent population and the sample mean, $\bar{x}$, is calculated.

Carry out hypotheses tests, given H_0 and H_1, at the significance level indicated.

	σ	n	$\bar{x}$	H_0	H_1	Sig. level
(i)	8	6	195	$\mu = 190$	$\mu > 190$	5%
(ii)	10	10	47.5	$\mu = 55$	$\mu < 55$	1%
(iii)	15	25	104.7	$\mu = 100$	$\mu \neq 100$	10%
(iv)	4.3	15	34.5	$\mu = 32$	$\mu > 32$	2%
(v)	40	12	345	$\mu = 370$	$\mu \neq 370$	5%

2 A machine is designed to make paperclips with mean mass 4.00 g and standard deviation 0.08 g. The distribution of the masses of the paperclips is Normal. Find
  (i) the probability that an individual paperclip, chosen at random, has mass greater than 4.04 g
  (ii) the standard error of the mass for random samples of 25 paperclips
  (iii) the probability that the mean mass of a random sample of 25 paperclips is greater than 4.04 g.

A quality control officer weighs a random sample of 25 paperclips and finds their total mass to be 101.2 g.
  (iv) Conduct a hypothesis test at the 5% significance level of whether this provides evidence of an increase in the mean mass of the paperclips. State your null and alternative hypotheses clearly.

3 It is known that the mass of a certain type of lizard has a Normal distribution with mean 72.7 g and standard deviation 4.8 g. A zoologist finds a colony of lizards in a remote place and is not sure whether they are of the same type. In order to test this, she collects a sample of 12 lizards and weighs them, with the following results.

80.4   67.2   74.9   78.8   76.5   75.5   80.2   81.9   79.3   70.0   69.2   69.1

  (i) Write down, in precise form, the zoologist's null and alternative hypotheses, and state whether a one-tail or two-tail test is appropriate.
  (ii) Carry out the test at the 5% significance level and write down your conclusion.
  (iii) Would your conclusion have been the same at the 10% significance level?

4 Observations over a long period of time have shown that the mid-day temperature at a particular place during the month of June is Normally distributed with a mean value of 23.9 °C with standard deviation 2.3 °C. An ecologist sets up an experiment to collect data for a hypothesis test of whether the climate is getting hotter. She selects at random 20 June days over a five-year period and records the mid-day temperature. Her results (in °C) are as follows.

| 20.1 | 26.2 | 23.3 | 28.9 | 30.4 | 28.4 | 17.3 | 22.7 | 25.1 | 24.2 |
| 15.4 | 26.3 | 19.3 | 24.0 | 19.9 | 30.3 | 32.1 | 26.7 | 27.6 | 23.1 |

(i) State the null and alternative hypotheses that the ecologist should use.

(ii) Carry out the test at the 10% significance level and state the conclusion.

(iii) Calculate the standard deviation of the sample data and comment on it.

5 A zoo has a long established colony of a particular type of rodent which is threatened with extinction in the wild. Observations over several years indicate that the life expectancy for the rodent is 470 days, with standard deviation 45 days. The staff at the zoo suspect that the life expectancy can be increased by improvements to the rodents' environment, and as an experiment allow 36 individuals to spend their whole lives in new surroundings. Their lifetimes are as follows.

491	505	523	470	468	567	512	560	468	498	471	444
511	508	508	421	465	499	486	513	500	488	487	455
523	516	486	478	470	465	487	572	451	513	483	474

(i) What do you need to assume about the parent population of lifetimes, of which the 36 is regarded as a random sample?

(ii) State the null and alternative hypotheses which these data have been collected to test.

(iii) Carry out the test at the 2% significance level and state the conclusion.

(iv) How could increased longevity help the rodent population to survive?

6 Some years ago the police did a large survey of the speeds of motorists along a stretch of motorway, timing cars between two bridges. They concluded that their mean speed was 80 mph with standard deviation 10 mph.

Recently the police wanted to investigate whether there had been any change in motorists' mean speed. They timed the first 20 green cars between the same two bridges and calculated their speeds (in mph) to be as follows.

| 85 | 75 | 80 | 102 | 78 | 96 | 124 | 70 | 68 | 92 |
| 84 | 69 | 73 | 78 | 86 | 92 | 108 | 78 | 80 | 84 |

(i) State an assumption you need to make about the speeds of motorists in the survey for the test to be valid.

(ii) State suitable null and alternative hypotheses and use the sample data to carry out a hypothesis test at the 5% significance level. State the conclusion.

One of the police officers involved in the investigation says that one of the cars in the sample was being driven exceptionally fast, and that its speed should not be included within the sample data.

(iii) Would the removal of this outlier alter the conclusion?

7 The keepers of a lighthouse were required to keep records of weather conditions. Analysis of their data from many years showed the visibility at mid-day to have a mean value of 14 sea miles with standard deviation 5.4 sea miles. A new keeper decided he would test his theory that the air had become less clear (and so visibility reduced) by carrying out a hypothesis test on data collected for his first 36 days on duty. His figures (in sea miles) were as follows.

35	21	12	7	2	1.5	1.5	1	0.25	0.25	15	17
18	20	16	11	8	8	9	17	35	35	4	0.25
0.25	5	11	28	35	35	16	2	1	0.5	0.5	1

(i) Write down a distributional assumption for the test to be valid.
(ii) Write down suitable null and alternative hypotheses.
(iii) Carry out the test at the 2.5% significance level and state the conclusion that the lighthouse keeper would have come to.
(iv) Criticise the sampling procedure used by the keeper and suggest a better one.

8 The weights of steaks sold by a supermarket are distributed Normally with mean μ and standard deviation 0.02 kg. A quality control inspector tests the hypothesis that $\mu = 1$ kg at the 5% level of significance. He takes a random sample of five steaks whose weights (in kg) are as follows.

$$0.977 \quad 1.014 \quad 0.989 \quad 0.972 \quad 0.968$$

His null hypothesis is that $\mu = 1$ kg, and he performs a two-tailed test. State his alternative hypothesis and perform the test.

Another inspector is employed to check that customers are not (on average) sold underweight steaks. If he had conducted a one-tailed test using the same random sample, the same level of significance and the same null hypothesis, what would have been his alternative hypothesis, and his conclusion?

[MEI]

9 A chemical is packed into bags by a machine. The mean weight of the bags is controlled by the machine operator, but the standard deviation is fixed at 0.96 kg. The mean weight should be 50 kg, but it is suspected that the machine has been set to give underweight bags. If a random sample of 36 bags has a total weight of 1789.20 kg, is there evidence to support the suspicion? (You must state the null and alternative hypotheses and you may assume that the weights of the bags are Normally distributed.)

[MEI]

10 Archaeologists have discovered that all skulls found in excavated sites in a certain country belong either to racial group *A* or to racial group *B*. The mean lengths of skulls from group *A* and group *B* are 190 mm and 196 mm respectively. The standard deviation for each group is 8 mm, and skull lengths are distributed Normally and independently.

A new excavation produced 12 skulls of mean length $\bar{x}$ and there is reason to believe that all these skulls belong to group *A*. It is required to test this belief statistically with the null hypothesis (H_0) that all the skulls belong to group *A* and the alternative hypothesis (H_1) that all the skulls belong to group *B*.

(i) State the distribution of the mean length of 12 skulls when H_0 is true.

(ii) Explain why a test of H_0 versus H_1 should take the form:

'Reject H_0 if $\bar{x} > c$',

where *c* is some critical value.

(iii) Calculate this critical value *c* to the nearest 0.1 mm when the probability of rejecting H_0 when it is in fact true is chosen to be 0.05.

(iv) Perform the test, given that the lengths (in mm) of the 12 skulls are as follows.

204.1 201.1 187.4 196.4 202.5 185.0
192.6 181.6 194.5 183.2 200.3 202.9

[MEI]

11 The packaging on a type of electric light bulb states that the average lifetime of the bulbs is 1000 hours. A consumer association thinks that this is an overestimate and tests a random sample of 64 bulbs, recording the lifetime, *x* hours, of each bulb. You may assume that the distribution of the bulbs' lifetimes is Normal.

The results are summarised as follows.

$$n = 64, \qquad \Sigma x = 63\,910.4, \qquad \Sigma x^2 = 63\,824\,061$$

(i) Calculate the mean and standard deviation of the data.

(ii) State suitable null and alternative hypotheses to test whether the statement on the packaging is overestimating the lifetime of this type of bulb.

(iii) Carry out the test, at the 5% significance level, stating your conclusions carefully.

12 A sample of 40 observations from a Normal distribution *X* gave $\Sigma x = 24$ and $\Sigma x^2 = 596$. Performing a two-tailed test at the 5% level, test whether the mean of the distribution is zero.

13 A random sample of 75 eleven-year-olds performed a simple task and the time taken, t minutes, noted for each. You may assume that the distribution of these times is Normal.

The results are summarised as follows.

$$n = 75, \qquad \Sigma t = 1215, \qquad \Sigma t^2 = 21\,708$$

(i) Calculate the mean and standard deviation of the data.

(ii) State suitable null and alternative hypotheses to test whether there is evidence that the mean time taken to perform this task is greater than 15 minutes.

(iii) Carry out the test, at the 1% significance level, stating your conclusions carefully.

14 Bags of sugar are supposed to contain, on average, 2 kg of sugar. A quality controller suspects that they actually contain less than this amount, and so 90 bags are taken at random and the mass, x kg, of sugar in each is measured. You may assume that the distribution of these masses is Normal.

The results are summarised as follows.

$$n = 90, \qquad \Sigma x = 177.9, \qquad \Sigma x^2 = 353.1916$$

(i) Calculate the mean and standard deviation of the data.

(ii) State suitable null and alternative hypotheses to test whether there is any evidence that the sugar is being sold 'underweight'.

(iii) Carry out the test, at the 2% significance level, stating your conclusions carefully.

15 A machine produces jars of skin cream, filled to a nominal volume of 100 ml. The machine is actually supposed to be set to 105 ml, to ensure that most jars actually contain more than the nominal volume of 100 ml. You may assume that the distribution of the volume of skin cream in a jar is Normal.

To check that the machine is correctly set, 80 jars are chosen at random, and the volume, x ml, of skin cream in each is measured.

The results are summarised as follows.

$$n = 80, \qquad \Sigma x = 8376, \qquad \Sigma x^2 = 877\,687$$

(i) Calculate the mean and standard deviation of the data.

(ii) State suitable null and alternative hypotheses for a test to see whether the machine appears to be set correctly.

(iii) Carry out the test, at the 10% significance level, stating your conclusions carefully.

Contingency tables

What kind of films do you enjoy?

To help it decide when to show trailers for future programmes, the management of a cinema asks its customers to fill out a brief questionnaire saying which type of film they enjoy. It wants to know whether there is any relationship between people's enjoyment of Horror films and Action movies. The management takes 150 randomly selected questionnaires and records whether those patrons enjoyed or did not enjoy Horror films and Action movies.

	Enjoyed Horror films	Did not enjoy Horror films
Enjoyed Action movies	51	41
Did not enjoy Action movies	15	43

This method of presenting data is called a 2×2 *contingency table* (later you will meet larger contingency tables). It is used where two variables (here 'attitude to Horror films' and 'attitude to Action movies') have been measured on a sample, and each variable can take two different values ('enjoy' or 'not enjoy').

The values of the variables fall into one or other of two categories. We want to determine the extent to which the variables are *related*.

It is conventional, and useful, to add the row and column totals in a contingency table: these are called the *marginal totals* of the table.

	Enjoyed Horror films	Did not enjoy Horror films	Marginal totals for Action movies
Enjoyed Action movies	51	41	92
Did not enjoy Action movies	15	43	58
Marginal totals for Horror films	66	84	150

At first sight, the data seem to support, for instance, the statement, 'Most people who enjoyed Horror films also enjoyed Action movies' – 51 out of 66 of them did. However, you know from your previous work on hypothesis testing that the purpose of collecting samples is to give evidence for or against statements about the population as a whole, not just to make comments about the results that appear in the sample.

A formal version of the cinema management's question is, 'Is enjoyment of Horror films independent of enjoyment of Action movies?'. You can use the sample data to investigate this question at the 1% significance level.

If enjoyment of the two types of film is independent, you would expect the probability of a randomly chosen cinema-goer enjoying both types of film to be the product of the probabilities of their enjoying each type. Formally, if p is the probability that a randomly chosen cinema-goer will enjoy Horror films and q is the probability that a randomly chosen cinema-goer will enjoy Action movies, then the joint distribution, on the assumption of independence, would be as shown in the table below

Probabilities that a cinema-goer	Enjoyed Horror films	Did not enjoy Horror films	Marginal probability
Enjoyed Action movies	pq	$(1-p)q$	q
Did not enjoy Action movies	$p(1-q)$	$(1-p)(1-q)$	$1-q$
Marginal probability	p	$1-p$	1

You can use the sample data to estimate the probabilities p and q. The number of cinema-goers in the sample who enjoyed Horror films is $51 + 15 = 66$, so the proportion of cinema-goers who enjoyed Horror films is $\frac{66}{150}$. The number of cinema-goers in the sample who enjoyed Action movies is $51 + 41 = 92$, so the proportion of cinema-goers who enjoyed Action movies is $\frac{92}{150}$.

Notice how you use the marginal totals 66 and 92 which were calculated previously.

If people enjoyed Horror films and Action movies independently with the probabilities you have just estimated, then you would expect to find, for instance,

Number of people enjoying both types

$$= 150 \times \text{P(a random person enjoying both types)}$$
$$= 150 \times \text{P(enjoying Horror)} \times \text{P(enjoying Action)}$$
$$= 150 \times \frac{66}{150} \times \frac{92}{150}$$
$$= \frac{6072}{150}$$
$$= 40.48$$

In the same way, you can calculate the number of people you would expect to correspond to each cell in the table.

Expected numbers	Enjoyed Horror films	Did not enjoy Horror films	Marginal totals for Action movies
Enjoyed Action movies	$150 \times \frac{66}{150} \times \frac{92}{150} = 40.48$	$150 \times \frac{84}{150} \times \frac{92}{150} = 51.52$	92
Did not enjoy Action movies	$150 \times \frac{66}{150} \times \frac{58}{150} = 25.52$	$150 \times \frac{84}{150} \times \frac{58}{150} = 32.48$	58
Marginal totals for Horror films	66	84	150

Note that it is an inevitable consequence of this calculation that these expected figures have the same marginal totals as the sample data.

You are now in a position to test the original hypotheses, which you can state formally as:

H_0: Enjoyment of the two types of film is independent.
H_1: Enjoyment of the two types of film is not independent.

The expected frequencies were calculated assuming the null hypothesis is true. You know the actual sample frequencies and the aim is to decide whether they are so different that the null hypothesis should be rejected.

A statistic which measures how far apart a set of observed frequencies is from the set expected under the null hypothesis is the χ^2 (chi-squared) statistic. It is given by the formula:

$$X^2 = \sum \frac{(\text{observed frequency} - \text{expected frequency})^2}{\text{expected frequency}} = \sum \frac{(f_o - f_e)^2}{f_e}.$$

You can use this here: the observed and expected frequencies are summarised below.

Observed frequencies	Enjoyed Horror	Did not enjoy Horror
Enjoyed Action	51	41
Did not enjoy Action	15	43

Expected frequencies	Enjoyed Horror	Did not enjoy Horror
Enjoyed Action	40.48	51.52
Did not enjoy Action	25.52	32.48

The χ^2 statistic is:

$$X^2 = \frac{(51 - 40.48)^2}{40.48} + \frac{(41 - 51.52)^2}{51.52} + \frac{(15 - 25.52)^2}{25.52} + \frac{(43 - 32.48)^2}{32.48}$$

$$= \frac{10.52^2}{40.48} + \frac{10.52^2}{51.52} + \frac{10.52^2}{25.52} + \frac{10.52^2}{32.48} = 12.626$$

Note

The four numerators in this calculation are equal. This is not by chance; it will always happen with a 2 × 2 table – and it is worth noting, as a useful calculational short cut.

Following the usual hypothesis-testing methodology, you want to know whether a value for this statistic at least as large as 12.626 is likely to occur by chance when the null hypothesis is true. For that, you need to know that, under H_0, the statistic X^2 is distributed with an approximate χ^2 distribution. The large expected number of people in each cell (all greater than 25) in this case means that the approximation is very good.

Critical values for the χ^2 distribution are given in tables but, before you can use them, you have to think about two more points.

What is the significance level of the test?

This should really have been set before any data were collected. If the management want at most a 1% chance of rejecting the null hypothesis when it is in fact true, then they will choose a 1% significance level.

How many degrees of freedom are involved?

The shape of the χ^2 distribution curve depends on the number of free variables involved, the degrees of freedom, v. (v is the Greek letter n and is pronounced 'new'.) To find the value for v you start off with the number of cells which must be filled and then subtract one degree of freedom for each restriction, derived from the data, which is placed on the frequencies. Here you are imposing the requirements that the total of the frequencies must be 150, and that the overall proportions of people enjoying Horror films and Action movies are $\frac{66}{150}$ and $\frac{92}{150}$ respectively.

Hence $v = 4$ (number of cells)

  $- 1$ (total of frequencies is fixed by the data)

  $- 2$ (proportions of people enjoying each type are estimated from the data)

  $= 1$

Looking in the tables for the 1% significance level and $v = 1$ gives a critical value of 6.635; see figure 3.7.

Since $12.626 > 6.635$, you reject the null hypothesis, H_0, and conclude that people's enjoyment of the two types of film is not independent or that the enjoyment of the two is *associated*. See figure 3.7 overleaf.

 Notice that you cannot conclude that enjoying one type of film *causes* people to enjoy the other. The test is of whether enjoyment of the two types is associated. It could be that a third factor, such as bloodthirstiness, causes both, but you do not know. The test tells you nothing about causality.

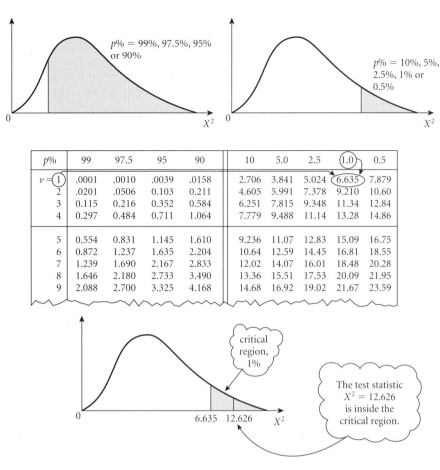

$p\%$	99	97.5	95	90	10	5.0	2.5	1.0	0.5
$v = 1$	.0001	.0010	.0039	.0158	2.706	3.841	5.024	6.635	7.879
2	.0201	.0506	0.103	0.211	4.605	5.991	7.378	9.210	10.60
3	0.115	0.216	0.352	0.584	6.251	7.815	9.348	11.34	12.84
4	0.297	0.484	0.711	1.064	7.779	9.488	11.14	13.28	14.86
5	0.554	0.831	1.145	1.610	9.236	11.07	12.83	15.09	16.75
6	0.872	1.237	1.635	2.204	10.64	12.59	14.45	16.81	18.55
7	1.239	1.690	2.167	2.833	12.02	14.07	16.01	18.48	20.28
8	1.646	2.180	2.733	3.490	13.36	15.51	17.53	20.09	21.95
9	2.088	2.700	3.325	4.168	14.68	16.92	19.02	21.67	23.59

Figure 3.7

Contingency tables in general

Suppose that two random variables, each taking values which fall into one of a
finite number of discrete categories, are both measured on the elements of a
sample. The table which results from listing the frequencies with which each
possible pair of values of the two variables arises is called a *contingency table*. If
the first variable can take m distinct values and the second can take n distinct
values, it is called an $m \times n$ *contingency table*.

The 4×3 contingency table on the next page shows the type of car (saloon,
sports, hatchback or estate) owned by 360 randomly-chosen people, and the age
category (under 30, 30–60, over 60) into which the owners fall.

	Age of driver			Marginal totals for car type
	under 30	30–60	over 60	
Saloon	10	67	57	134
Sports car	19	14	3	36
Hatchback	32	47	34	113
Estate	7	56	14	77
Marginal totals for age category	68	184	108	360

The marginal totals are not essential in a contingency table, but it is conventional – and convenient – to add them.

The χ^2 test for independence in a contingency table

Given the data in a contingency table it is possible to test the hypotheses:

H_0: The two variables whose values are being measured are independent in the population.

H_1: The two variables whose values are being measured are not independent in the population.

EXAMPLE 3.4

Use the data in the contingency table above to test, at the 5% significance level, the hypotheses:
H_0: Car type is independent of owner's age.
H_1: Car type is not independent of owner's age.

SOLUTION

Step 1
You need to calculate the expected frequencies in the table assuming the null hypothesis is true. You use the probability estimates given by the marginal totals, for instance:

Probability car type is a hatchback $= \frac{113}{360}$.

Probability driver's age is over 60 $= \frac{108}{360}$.

The expected frequencies are then calculated as overleaf.

Expected frequency of hatchback and owner's age over 60

$= 360 \times$ P(car is a hatchback and owner's age over 60)

$= 360 \times$ P(car is a hatchback) $\times$ P(owner's age over 60) ←

$= 360 \times \dfrac{113}{360} \times \dfrac{108}{360} = \dfrac{113 \times 108}{360}$

Since, under the null hypothesis, the type of car and the driver's age are independent.

This illustrates the general result for contingency tables:

$$\text{Expected frequency in a cell} = \frac{\text{product of marginal totals for that cell}}{\text{number of observations}}.$$

The table below shows all the expected frequencies, calculated in this way.

	Age of driver			Marginal totals for car type
	under 30	30–60	over 60	
Saloon	25.311	68.489	40.200	134
Sports car	6.800	18.400	10.800	36
Hatchback	21.344	57.756	33.900	113
Estate	14.544	39.356	23.100	77
Marginal totals for age category	68	184	108	360

Step 2
At this point it is important to check that all the frequencies are large enough to make the χ^2 distribution a good approximation to the distribution of the X^2 statistic – the usual rule of thumb is to require all the expected frequencies to be greater than 5. This requirement is (just) satisfied here – though you might be cautious in your conclusions if the X^2 statistic is very near the relevant critical value. If some of the cells have small expected frequencies, you should either collect more data or amalgamate some of the categories if it makes sense to do so. For instance, two adjacent age ranges could reasonably be combined, but two car types probably could not.

Step 3
The value of the X^2 statistic is, as before:

$$X^2 = \sum \frac{(\text{observed frequency} - \text{expected frequency})^2}{\text{expected frequency}}$$

$$= \frac{(10 - 25.311)^2}{25.311} + \frac{(67 - 68.489)^2}{68.489} + \dots \text{ etc.}$$

$$= 9.262 + 0.032 + \dots \text{ etc.}$$

Unfortunately, unlike the 2×2 special case, there is no shortcut to this calculation – the numerators are *not* equal. The table below shows the value of $\dfrac{(\text{observed frequency} - \text{expected frequency})^2}{\text{expected frequency}}$ for each cell.

	Age of driver		
	under 30	**30–60**	**over 60**
Saloon	9.262	0.032	7.021
Sports car	21.888	1.052	5.633
Hatchback	5.319	2.003	0.000
Estate	3.913	7.039	3.585

The sum of these values is $X^2 = 66.749$.

Step 4
The degrees of freedom must be calculated.

There are $3 \times 4 = 12$ cells in the contingency table, so there are twelve possibilities for differences between the observed and expected tables: however, not all these twelve differences are independent because all the marginal totals are automatically the same in observed and expected tables. There are $3 + 4 = 7$ marginal totals, but only $7 - 1 = 6$ of these are independent, because the row totals and column totals must both give the same overall total (360 in this case). This means that the twelve initial possibilities for difference are reduced to $12 - (7 - 1) = 6$ independent possibilities which means there are 6 degrees of freedom.

In general, for an $m \times n$ table, the degrees of freedom is:

$$v = m \times n \quad \longleftarrow \quad \text{number of cells}$$

$$- (m + n - 1) \quad \longleftarrow \quad \begin{array}{c}\text{Row and column totals are} \\ \text{fixed but row totals and column} \\ \text{totals have the same sum.}\end{array}$$

$$= mn - m - n + 1$$
$$= (m - 1)(n - 1)$$

Step 5
From the χ^2 tables, the critical value at the 5% level with six degrees of freedom is 12.59. The observed X^2 statistic is 66.749 which is greater than the critical value and so you reject the null hypothesis and accept that car type is not independent of owner's age, or that car type and owner's age are associated.

Note

It is not obvious *how* the lack of independence arises: you have not demonstrated, for example, that increasing age of the owner is associated with less sporty cars. All you can say is that the observations were very different from what you would expect from independence of the variables, and so this independence is not plausible.

However, by looking at the values of $\dfrac{(\text{observed frequency} - \text{expected frequency})^2}{\text{expected frequency}}$

for each cell calculated in Step 3 above you can see which differences between observed and expected frequencies are significant, in the sense of making a large contribution to the X^2 statistic. In this case, the under-30 age group own fewer saloon and estate cars, more hatchbacks and many more sports cars than expected. Other cells with relatively large contributions to the X^2 statistic correspond to estate cars being owned more often than expected by 30–60-year-olds, and less often than expected by older or younger drivers, and over-60s owning more saloon cars and fewer sports cars than expected.

 Using a graphic calculator

It is fairly easy to carry out a χ^2 test for a contingency table using a graphic calculator.

Figure 3.8 shows the output for Example 3.4 obtained by carrying out the following steps.

1 Enter the observed frequencies into matrix A.
2 Display the χ^2 test menu screen.
3 Display the expected frequencies in matrix B.
4 Display the results of the χ^2 test.

Test statistic:	$X^2 = 66.749\ldots$
$P(\chi^2 > 66.749\ldots)$	$p = 1.894\ldots \times 10^{-12}$
Degrees of freedom:	$df = 6$

5 Display the associated χ^2 curve and shade the area corresponding to $P(X^2 > 66.749\ldots)$.

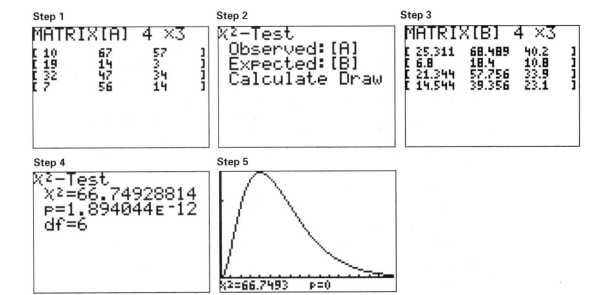

Step 1

```
MATRIX[A]  4 ×3
[ 10     67     57   ]
[ 19     14      3   ]
[ 32     47     34   ]
[ 7      56     14   ]
```

Step 2

```
X²-Test
 Observed: [A]
 Expected: [B]
 Calculate Draw
```

Step 3

```
MATRIX[B]  4 ×3
[ 25.311  68.489  40.2  ]
[ 6.8     18.4    10.8  ]
[ 21.344  57.756  33.9  ]
[ 14.544  39.356  23.1  ]
```

Step 4

```
X²-Test
 X²=66.74928814
 P=1.894044E-12
 df=6
```

Step 5

```
X²=66.7493     P=0
```

Figure 3.8

> *Note*
>
> The illustrations above are taken from a TI-83 graphic calculator. Similar screen shots are possible from other graphic calculators.

Using a spreadsheet

An interactive spreadsheet is a good medium to carry out the steps of a χ^2 test for a contingency table.

You need to enter
- the observed frequencies
- the significance level.

The spreadsheet will display
- the expected frequencies
- the contributions to the X^2 statistic
- the degrees of freedom and the critical value
- the results of the test together with the conclusion.

The spreadsheet below shows the output for Example 3.4.

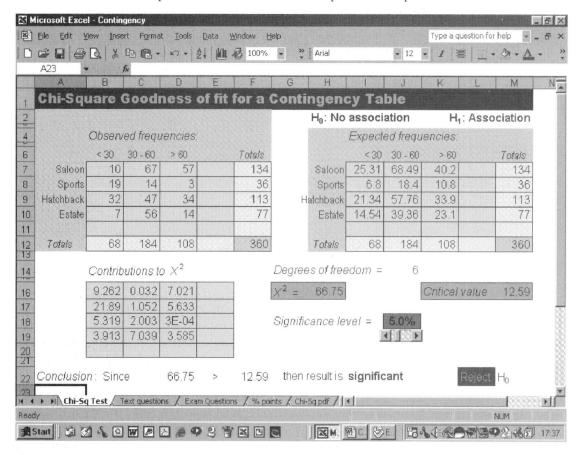

Figure 3.9

1 A medical insurance company office is the largest employer in a small town. When 37 randomly-chosen people living in the town were asked where they worked and whether they belonged to the town's health club, 21 were found to work for the insurance company, of whom 15 also belonged to the health club, while 7 of the 16 not working for the insurance company belonged to the health club.

Test the hypothesis that health club membership is independent of employment by the medical insurance company.

2 A group of 281 voters is asked to rate how good a job they think the Prime Minister is doing. Each is also asked for the highest educational qualifications they have achieved. The frequencies with which responses occurred are shown in the table.

	Highest qualifications achieved			
Rating of PM	None	GCSE or equivalent	A-level or equivalent	Degree or equivalent
Very poor	11	37	13	6
Poor	12	17	22	8
Moderate	7	11	25	10
Good	10	17	17	9
Very good	19	16	8	6

Use these figures to test whether there is an association between rating of the Prime Minister and highest educational qualifications achieved.

3 In a random sample of 163 adult males, 37 suffer from hay-fever and 51 from asthma, both figures including 14 men who suffer from both. Test whether the two conditions are associated.

4 In a survey of 184 London residents brought up outside the south east of England, respondents were asked whether, job and family permitting, they would like to return to their area of origin. Their responses are shown in the table.

Region of origin	Would like to return to	Would not like to return to
South-west	16	28
Midlands	22	35
North	15	31
Wales	8	6
Scotland	14	9

Test the hypothesis that desire to return is independent of region of origin.

5 A sample of 80 men and 150 women selected at random are tested for colour-blindness. Twelve of the men and five of the women are found to be colour-blind. Is there evidence at the 1% level that colour-blindness is sex-related?

6 Depressive illness is categorised as type I, II or III. In a group of depressive psychiatric patients, the length of time for which their symptoms are apparent is observed. The results are shown below.

Length of depressive episode	Type of symptoms		
	I	II	III
Brief	15	22	12
Average	30	19	26
Extended	7	13	21
Semi-permanent	6	9	11

Is the length of the depressive episode independent of the type of symptoms?

7 The personnel manager of a large firm is investigating whether there is any association between the length of service of the employees and the type of training they receive from the firm. A random sample of 200 employee records is taken from the last few years and is classified according to these criteria. Length of service is classified as short (meaning less than 1 year), medium (1–3 years) and long (more than 3 years). Type of training is classified as being merely an initial 'induction course', proper initial on-the-job training but little if any more, and regular and continuous training. The data are as follows.

Type of training	Length of service		
	Short	Medium	Long
Induction course	14	23	13
Initial on-the-job	12	7	13
Continuous	28	32	58

Examine at the 5% level of significance whether these data provide evidence of association between length of service and type of training, stating clearly your null and alternative hypotheses.

Discuss your conclusions.

8 The bank manager at a large branch was investigating the incidence of bad debts. Many loans had been made during the past year; the manager inspected the records of a random sample of 100 loans, and broadly classified them as satisfactory or unsatisfactory loans and as having been made to private individuals, small businesses or large businesses. The data were as follows.

	Satifactory	Unsatifactory
Private individual	22	4
Small business	34	13
Large business	24	4

Carry out a χ^2 test at the 5% level of significance to examine if there is any association between whether or not the loan was satisfactory and the type of customer to whom the loan was made. State clearly the null and alternative hypotheses and the critical value of the test statistic.

9 In the initial stages of a market research exercise to investigate whether a proposed advertising campaign would be worthwhile, a survey of newspaper readership was undertaken. 100 people selected at random from the target population were interviewed. They were asked how many newspapers they read regularly. They were also classified as to whether they lived in urban or rural areas. The results were as follows.

Number of newspapers read regularly	Urban	Rural
None	15	11
One	22	18
More than one	27	7

(i) Examine at the 10% level of significance whether these data provide evidence of an association between the categories. State clearly the null and alternative hypotheses you are testing.

(ii) Justify the degrees of freedom for the test.

(iii) Discuss the conclusions reached from the test.

10 Public health officers are monitoring air quality over a large area. Air quality measurements using mobile instruments are made frequently by officers touring the area. The air quality is classified as poor, reasonable, good or excellent. The measurement sites are classified as being in residential areas, industrial areas, commercial areas or rural areas. The table shows a sample of frequencies over an extended period. The row and column totals and the grand total are also shown.

Measurement site	Air quality				
	Poor	Reasonable	Good	Excellent	Row totals
Residential	107	177	94	22	400
Industrial	87	128	74	19	308
Commercial	133	228	148	51	560
Rural	21	71	24	16	132
Column totals	348	604	340	108	1400

Examine at the 5% level of significance whether or not there is any association between measurement site and air quality, stating carefully the null and alternative hypotheses you are testing. Report briefly on your conclusions.

11 In an investigation of small business development in England, researchers are examining whether there is any association between the geographical area where such a business is located and the lifespan of the business. A random sample of records has been obtained from a national database. The geographical areas are classified very broadly as South-east, Midlands, North and 'Rest'. Lifespans are classified as short, medium and long. The table shows the frequencies obtained in the sample; row and column totals and the grand total are also shown.

Geographical area	Lifespan of business			Row totals
	Short	Medium	Long	
South-east	140	72	56	268
Midlands	104	53	45	202
North	71	51	48	170
Rest	57	48	59	164
Column totals	372	224	208	804

Examine at the 1% level of significance whether or not there is any association between geographical area and lifespan, stating carefully the null and alternative hypotheses you are testing. Report briefly on your conclusions.

[MEI]

1 An electrical component is specified by the manufacturers as having a mean lifetime of at least 1000 hours. The manufacturers regularly find the mean lifetimes for batches of five components to guard against components falling below specification. In performing hypothesis tests they rely on past records which show that lifetimes are Normally distributed with a standard deviation of 37 hours.

(i) Write down the null and alternative hypotheses under test.

(ii) Explain why no formal hypothesis test would be required for a batch with mean lifetime of 1010 hours.

(iii) Carry out an appropriate hypothesis test at the 5% level of significance for a batch of five components with a mean lifetime of 973 hours.

[MEI, *part*]

2 When watching games of men's basketball, I have noticed that the players are often tall. I am interested to find out whether or not men who play basketball really are taller than men in general.

I know that the heights, in metres, of men in general have the distribution $N(1.73, 0.08^2)$. I make the assumption that the heights, X metres, of male basketball players are also Normally distributed, with the same variance as the heights of men in general, but possibly with a larger mean.

(i) Write down the null and alternative hypotheses under test.

I propose to base my test on the heights of eight male basketball players who recently appeared for our local team and I shall use a 5% level of significance.

(ii) Write down the distribution of the sample mean, X, for samples of size 8 drawn from the distribution of X, assuming the null hypothesis is true.

(iii) Determine the critical region for my test, illustrating your answer with a sketch.

(iv) Carry out the test, given that the mean height of the eight players is 1.765 m. You should present your conclusions carefully, stating any additional assumption you need to make.

[MEI, *part*]

3 The error in the readings made on a measuring instrument can be modelled by the continuous random variable X which has a Normal distribution with mean μ and standard deviation σ. If the instrument is correctly calibrated then $\mu = 0$.

In order to check the calibration of the instrument, the errors in a random sample of 40 readings were determined. These data are summarised as follows.

$$\sum x = 120, \qquad \sum x^2 = 3285$$

(i) Estimate σ^2.

(ii) State suitable null and alternative hypotheses to test whether or not the machine is correctly calibrated.

(iii) Carry out the test, at the 5% significance level, stating your conclusions carefully.

(iv) Suppose the data from the 40 readings had been such that the estimate of σ^2 as found in part **(i)** was larger, but without changing the sample mean. State the effect this would have on the value of the test statistic in part **(iii)**. Explain why this might affect the conclusion to part **(iii)**.

[MEI, *adapted*]

4 The amounts of money spent by customers on meals at a certain restaurant are Normally distributed with mean and standard deviation (in pence) 1424 and 108 respectively. The manager introduces new menus in the hope of increasing the amount spent. It is assumed that the standard deviation remains the same.

After the introduction of the new menus, the amounts spent by a random sample of 20 customers are found to have mean 1465 pence.

(i) State suitable null and alternative hypotheses to test whether the mean amount spent by customers has increased.

(ii) Carry out the test, at the 5% significance level, stating your conclusions carefully.

[MEI, *adapted*]

5 The length of rods used in an engineering structure is specified as being 40 cm. It does not matter if the rods are slightly longer, but they should not be any shorter. These rods are made by a machine in such a way that their lengths are Normally distributed with standard deviation 0.2 cm. An operator sets the machine so that the mean length, μ cm, is slightly greater than 40.

The operator takes a random sample of 12 rods. Their lengths, in centimetres, are as follows.

40.43	40.49	40.19	40.36	40.81	40.47
40.46	40.63	40.41	40.27	40.34	40.54

The operator wishes to examine whether μ may be assumed to be 40.5, as experience shows that a smaller mean would not give an adequate margin for error.

(i) State suitable null and alternative hypotheses for the test.

(ii) Carry out the test, at the 5% significance level, stating your conclusions carefully.

[MEI, *part*]

6 An industrial process requires the extrusion of a small amount of plastic on to a metal surface so that an air-tight sealed joint can be made with another surface. The mass of plastic extruded is critical and is specified as being 1.32 grams. If it is too small, a properly sealed joint cannot be made; if it is too large, bumps and ridges tend to form on the plastic so that again the joint is not properly sealed.

It is understood that the variations in the masses extruded are well modelled by a Normal distribution and that its standard deviation is 0.03 grams.

An inspector examines a random sample of the extrusions and records their masses, which are as follows (in grams).

1.30	1.26	1.33	1.32	1.35
1.29	1.31	1.28	1.36	1.30

(i) State suitable null and alternative hypotheses for a test to examine whether the mean mass extruded is as specified.

(ii) Carry out the test, at the 5% significance level, stating your conclusions carefully.

(iii) Show that the critical region for the test consists of values of the sample mean outside the range (1.3014, 1.3386).

[**MEI**, *part*]

7 A factory manager is specifying a new storage tank for a particular chemical. In routine use, the tank will be filled to capacity each weekend. There should be enough chemical to last until the next weekend, as emergency deliveries are very expensive. On the other hand, money is wasted if an excessive amount of chemical is stored.

The volume of chemical required varies from week to week and is modelled by a Normally distributed random variable X. The manager is investigating the mean of X. Data are available for a random sample of 15 weeks, giving the volumes of the chemical used in each week. These are as follows (in litres).

1962	1928	1943	1939	1866
1964	1942	1996	1909	1940
1897	1924	1978	1944	1992

The standard deviation of X is taken from long experience to be 28 litres. A 2000-litre tank will be specified if the mean of X is no more than 1930 litres.

(i) State suitable null and alternative hypotheses to test whether a 2000-litre tank should be specified.

(ii) Carry out the test, at the 5% significance level, stating your conclusions carefully.

[**MEI**, *part*]

8 A sports and social club provides indoor and outdoor courts for racquet sports (tennis, etc.), a gymnasium and general social facilities. Members can join as individuals, as family members or as business members. In a survey conducted by the club management, a large sample of members were asked what the primary reason was for their joining the club. The results were as follows.

		Primary reason			
		Indoor courts	Outdoor courts	Gymnasium	Social facilities
Type of member	Individual	42	11	46	7
	Family	99	20	82	21
	Business	27	3	22	16

(i) Examine whether or not there is any association between type of member and primary reason. State carefully the null and alternative hypotheses you are testing, and give the approximate level of significance of the data.

(ii) Discuss your conclusions.

[MEI]

9 The marketing manager at a theme park undertakes a survey of a random sample of 200 visitors. As part of the analysis, he categorises them as local people, people who have come a medium distance or people who have come a long distance, with a separate category of people in coach parties. He also categorises them according to the amount of money they spend in the park, as light, medium or heavy spenders. A table displaying the results is as follows.

		Amount spent		
		Light	Medium	Heavy
Distance	Local	17	23	16
	Medium distance	15	25	34
	Long distance	4	16	12
	Coach party	8	22	8

(i) Stating your null and alternative hypotheses, examine whether or not there is any association between 'distance' and 'amount spent'. Use a 10% significance level.

(ii) Discuss your conclusions.

[MEI]

10 The managers of a waste disposal site are carrying out a survey of usage. Each member of a random sample of people using the site is asked where they have come from. The site is meant to serve two local authorities, A and B, but it is known that users also come from elsewhere. Each member of the sample is also asked the main purpose of the visit, categorised as disposal of household rubbish, of garden waste, of recyclable materials and of old appliances such as worn-out refrigerators. The results are as follows.

		Main purpose of visit			
		Household rubbish	Garden waste	Recyclable materials	Old appliances
Origin	A	30	27	16	8
	B	15	28	13	7
	Other areas	8	8	9	11

(i) State the null and alternative hypotheses under examination in the usual χ^2 test of whether or not there is association between 'origin' and 'main purpose of visit'.

(ii) Carry out the usual test, at the 5% significance level.

(iii) Discuss your conclusions.

(iv) Explain briefly *why*, in a contingency table of this type, the expected frequencies are calculated in the way that they are.

[MEI]

11 An insurance broker is investigating whether the amounts of money paid out in respect of claims for personal accidents are related to the circumstances of the accidents.

Payouts are classified as high, medium or low. Circumstances of accidents are classified as work-related, travel-related, home-related or other. Data for a random sample of 200 claims are shown in the table.

		Circumstances of accident			
		Work-related	Travel-related	Home-related	Other
Payout	High	40	7	26	15
	Medium	22	9	4	17
	Low	14	10	18	18

(i) State the null and alternative hypotheses under examination in the usual χ^2 test applied to this contingency table.

(ii) Carry out the usual test, at the 5% significance level.

(iii) Discuss your conclusions.

[MEI]

12 A random sample of 60 people who had been treated for drug abuse were monitored after their treatment. These people were classified according to whether they had received more or less than 15 years of full-time education, and the numbers in each category who were subsequently convicted of a criminal offence were also recorded. The results are given in the following table.

	Full-time education	
	15 years or more	Less than 15 years
Subsequent conviction	16	20
No subsequent conviction	6	18

Test, at the 5% significance level, the hypothesis that subsequent conviction is independent of the amount of full-time education received.

[OCR]

13 A random sample of 200 teachers in Higher Education, Secondary Schools and Primary Schools gave the following numbers of men and women in each sector.

	Higher Education	Secondary Schools	Primary Schools
Men	21	39	20
Women	13	55	52

(i) State the null and alternative hypotheses under examination in the usual χ^2 test of whether or not there is association between 'age group taught' and 'gender'.

(ii) Carry out the usual test, at the 1% significance level, stating your conclusion carefully.

(iii) Identify which cell makes the greatest contribution to the total value of the test statistic. Hence comment on the association between 'age group taught' and 'gender'.

[OCR]

1 Distribution of sample means

- For samples of size n drawn from a Normal distribution with mean μ and finite variance σ^2, the distribution of sample means is Normal with mean μ and variance $\dfrac{\sigma^2}{n}$, i.e. $\bar{x} \sim \text{N}\left(\mu, \dfrac{\sigma^2}{n}\right)$.

- The standard error of the mean (i.e. the standard deviation of the sample means) is given by $\dfrac{\sigma}{\sqrt{n}}$.

2 Hypothesis testing

- Sample data may be used to carry out a hypothesis test on the null hypothesis that the population mean has some particular value, μ_0, i.e. $H_0: \mu = \mu_0$.

- The test statistic is $z = \dfrac{\bar{x} - \mu_0}{\dfrac{\sigma}{\sqrt{n}}}$ and the Normal distribution is used.

3 Contingency tables

- An $m \times n$ *contingency table* results when two variables are measured on a sample with the first variable having m possible categories of results and the second variable having n possible categories of results. Each *cell* of the table contains an *observed frequency* with which that pair of categories of values of the two variables occurs in the sample.

- To test whether the variables in an $m \times n$ contingency table are independent the steps are as follows.

  (i) The null hypothesis is that the variables are independent, the alternative is that they are not.

  (ii) Calculate the marginal (row and column) totals for the table.

  (iii) Calculate the *expected frequency* in each cell as
  $$\frac{\text{row total} \times \text{column total}}{\text{total sample size}}$$

  (iv) The X^2 statistic is $\displaystyle\sum \frac{(f_o - f_e)^2}{f_e}$ where f_o is the observed frequency and f_e the expected frequency in each cell.

  (v) The *degrees of freedom*, v, for the test is $(m-1)(n-1)$ for an $m \times n$ table.

  (vi) Read the critical value from the χ^2 tables for the appropriate degrees of freedom and significance level. If X^2 is less than the significance level, the null hypothesis is accepted; otherwise it is rejected.

  (vii) If two variables are not independent you say that there is an *association* between them.

4

Bivariate data

It is now proved beyond doubt that smoking is one of the leading causes of statistics.

John Peers

THE AVONFORD STAR

Ferguson to sign two new strikers

Tom Ferguson the manager of Avonford Rovers Football club, is set to sign two strikers in his bid to win promotion to the Assembly League next season. A buoyant Tom Ferguson told me this morning 'You have to score a lot of goals in this game and then the points will look after themselves. It's the same at all levels of the game, from the Premiership down.'

Tony Shields, from Walkden, has just recovered from a bunion operation and is the man Tom has in mind to lead the attack. At 195 cm tall he is formidable at set pieces and in the attacking half of the field. His strike partner will be Harry Gregory from Middle Fishbrook. Tom wants to sign Gregory before one of the big clubs come in and make him an offer. Ferguson told me, 'Gregory is only 160 cm tall but is like greased lightning around the box. People will probably call our new partnership Little and Large, but let's hope they score plenty of goals and then we'll be all right.'

Tony Shields clashes with Lumumba Athletic keeper Fred Weaver

❓ Do you agree with Tom Ferguson that if your team can score a lot of goals then the points total will look after itself?

Tom says it's the same principle from the Premiership down – so let us put the Premiership to the test. Here are the final positions and details of all clubs at the end of the 2003–04 season.

	P	W	D	L	F	A	Pts
Arsenal	38	26	12	0	73	26	90
Chelsea	38	24	7	7	67	30	79
Manchester United	38	23	6	9	64	35	75
Liverpool	38	16	12	10	55	37	60
Newcastle United	38	13	17	8	52	40	56
Aston Villa	38	15	11	12	48	44	56
Charlton Athletic	38	14	11	13	51	51	53
Bolton Wanderers	38	14	11	13	48	56	53
Fulham	38	14	10	14	52	46	52
Birmingham City	38	12	14	12	43	48	50
Middlesbrough	38	13	9	16	44	52	48
Southampton	38	12	11	15	44	45	47
Portsmouth	38	12	9	17	47	54	45
Tottenham Hotspur	38	13	6	19	47	57	45
Blackburn Rovers	38	12	8	18	51	59	44
Manchester City	38	9	14	15	55	54	41
Everton	38	9	12	17	45	57	39
Leicester City	38	6	15	17	48	65	33
Leeds United	38	8	9	21	40	79	33
Wolverhampton Wanderers	38	7	12	19	38	77	33

The graph in figure 4.1 illustrates the goals scored and points total for all 20 competing teams.

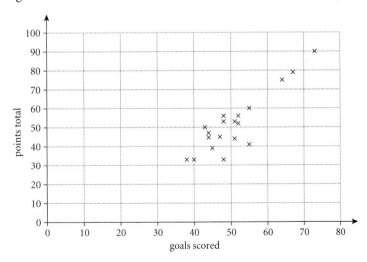

Figure 4.1 Scatter diagram showing goals scored and points total for all teams in the Premiership 2003–04 season

Looking at the spread of data points it does seem that the teams scoring many goals are the teams with the highest points totals.

The data in this example are a set of pairs of values for the two variables, the goals scored and the points totals of all the teams in the 2003–04 football Premiership. This is an example of *bivariate data*, where each item in the sample requires the values of two variables. The graph in figure 4.1 is called a *scatter diagram* and this is a common way of showing bivariate data.

If each point lies on a straight line, then there is said to be perfect *linear correlation* between the two variables. It is much more likely, however, that your data fall close to a straight line but not exactly on it. The better the fit, the higher the level of linear correlation.

Describing variables

Dependent and independent variables

The scatter diagram in figure 4.1 was drawn with the goals scored on the horizontal axis and the points total on the vertical axis. It was done that way to emphasise that the number of points is dependent upon the number of goals scored. (A team gains points as a result of scoring goals. It does not score goals as a result of gaining points.) It is normal practice to plot the *dependent* variable on the vertical (y) axis and the *independent* variable on the horizontal (x) axis.

Here are some more examples of dependent and independent variables.

Independent variable	Dependent variable
Number of people in a lift	Total weight of passengers
The amount of rain falling on a field whilst the crop is growing	The weight of the crop yielded
The number of people visiting a bar in an evening	The volume of beer sold

Random and non-random variables

In the examples above, both the variables have unpredictable values and so are *random*. The same is true for the example about goals scored and points totals in football. Both variables are random variables, free to assume any of a particular set of discrete values in a given range. All that follows about *correlation* will assume that both variables are random.

Sometimes, one or both of the variables is *controlled*, so that the variable only assumes a set of predetermined values; for example, the times at which temperature measurements are taken at a meteorological station. Controlled variables are *non-random*. Situations in which the independent variable is controlled and the dependent variable is random form the basis of *regression* analysis.

This chapter examines situations where *either* correlation *or* regression analysis is appropriate.

Interpreting scatter diagrams

You can often judge if correlation is present just by looking at a scatter diagram.

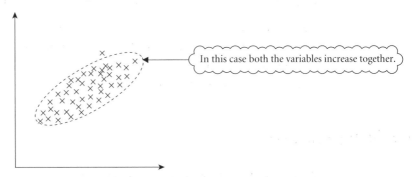

Figure 4.2 Positive correlation

Notice that in figure 4.2 almost all the observation points can be contained within an ellipse. This shape often arises when both variables are random. You should look for it before going on to do a calculation of Pearson's product moment correlation coefficient (see page 111). The narrower the elliptical profile, the greater the correlation.

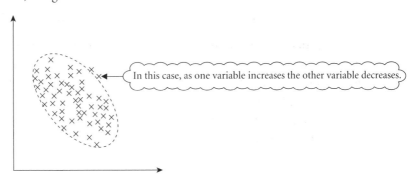

Figure 4.3 Negative correlation

In figure 4.3 the points again fall into an elliptical profile and this time there is negative correlation. The fatter ellipse in this diagram indicates weaker correlation than in the case shown in figure 4.2.

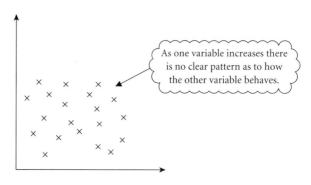

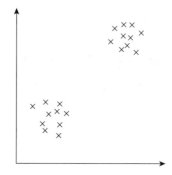

Figure 4.4 No correlation

In the case illustrated in figure 4.4 the points fall randomly in the (x, y) plane and there appears to be no association between the variables.

 You should be aware of some distributions which at first sight appear to indicate linear correlation but in fact do not.

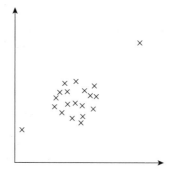

Figure 4.5 Two islands

This scatter diagram is probably showing two quite different groups, neither of them having any correlation.

Figure 4.6 Outliers

This is a small data set with no correlation. However, the two outliers give the impression that there is positive linear correlation.

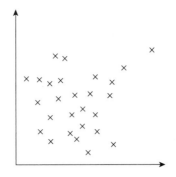

Figure 4.7 A funnel-shaped distribution

The bulk of these data have no correlation but a few items give the impression that there is correlation.

Note

In none of these three false cases is the distribution even approximately elliptical.

There are many situations you can investigate for yourself. Here are two which you can carry out with a group of your friends.

Dice

Toss a pair of ordinary but distinguishable dice, A and B, 100 times and record the following data for each toss:

(i) the score on die A
(ii) the total score on the two dice
(iii) the difference between the scores on the two dice.

Plot three scatter diagrams to compare **(i)** and **(ii)**; **(i)** and **(iii)**; **(ii)** and **(iii)**. Are you able to draw any conclusions about the relationships between the data?

Brains

Select a group of students of about the same age.

For each student, find the circumference of his or her head and the total time spent doing homework in the last week. Plot the data on a scatter diagram. Do you think there is a hint of correlation present?

Product moment correlation

The scatter diagram in figure 4.1 revealed that there may be a mutual association between the goals scored and the points totals of teams in the Premiership at the end of the 2003–04 season. This section sets out to quantify that relationship. Figure 4.8 shows this scatter diagram again.

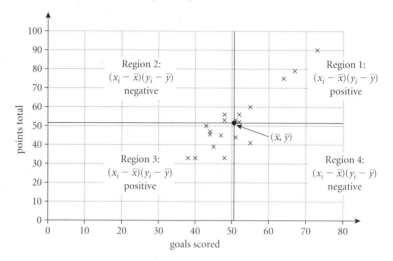

Figure 4.8

The mean number of goals scored is

$$\bar{x} = \frac{\Sigma x_i}{n} = \frac{73 + 67 + 64 + \ldots + 38}{20}$$

$$= \frac{1012}{20}$$

$$= 50.6.$$

The mean points total is

$$\bar{y} = \frac{\Sigma y_i}{n} = \frac{90 + 79 + 75 + \ldots + 33}{20}$$

$$= \frac{1032}{20}$$

$$= 51.6.$$

(x_i, y_i) are the various data points, for example (48, 53) for Bolton Wanderers; n is the number of such points, in this case 20, one for each club in the Premiership.

You will see that the point $(\bar{x}, \bar{y})$ has also been plotted on the scatter diagram and lines drawn through this point parallel to the axes. These lines divide the scatter diagram into four regions.

You can think of the point $(\bar{x}, \bar{y})$ as the middle of the scatter diagram and so treat it as a new origin. Relative to $(\bar{x}, \bar{y})$, the co-ordinates of the various points are all of the form $(x_i - \bar{x}, y_i - \bar{y})$.

In regions 1 and 3 the product $(x_i - \bar{x})(y_i - \bar{y})$ is positive for every point.

In regions 2 and 4 the product $(x_i - \bar{x})(y_i - \bar{y})$ is negative for every point.

When there is positive correlation most or all of the data points will fall in regions 1 and 3 and so you would expect the sum of these terms to be positive and large. This sum is denoted by S_{xy}.

$$S_{xy} = \sum_{i=1}^{n} (x_i - \bar{x})(y_i - \bar{y})$$

When there is negative correlation most or all of the points will be in regions 2 and 4 and so you would expect the sum of these terms (in the equation above) to be negative and large.

When there is little or no correlation the points will be scattered round all four regions. Those in regions 1 and 3 will result in positive values of $(x_i - \bar{x})(y_i - \bar{y})$ but when you add these to the negative values from the points in regions 2 and 4 you would expect most of them to cancel each other out. Consequently the total value of all the terms should be small.

By itself the actual value of S_{xy} does not tell you very much because:

- no allowance has been made for the number of items of data
- no allowance has been made for the spread within the data
- no allowance has been made for the units of x and y.

Pearson's product moment correlation coefficient

To allow for both the number of items and the spread within the data, together with the units of x and y, the value of S_{xy} is divided by the square root of the product of S_{xx} and S_{yy}.

The sample product moment correlation coefficient is denoted by r and is given by

$$r = \frac{S_{xy}}{\sqrt{S_{xx}S_{yy}}} = \frac{\Sigma(x_i - \bar{x})(y_i - \bar{y})}{\sqrt{\Sigma(x_i - \bar{x})^2 \Sigma(y_i - \bar{y})^2}} = \frac{\Sigma x_i y_i - n\bar{x}\,\bar{y}}{\sqrt{(\Sigma x_i^2 - n\bar{x}^2)(\Sigma y_i^2 - n\bar{y}^2)}}.$$

As with data analysis in *Statistics 1*, if there is no ambiguity in the summations, the subscript i is often omitted, to give formulae for r as

$$r = \frac{S_{xy}}{\sqrt{S_{xx}S_{yy}}} = \frac{\Sigma(x - \bar{x})(y - \bar{y})}{\sqrt{\Sigma(x - \bar{x})^2 \Sigma(y - \bar{y})^2}} = \frac{\Sigma xy - n\bar{x}\,\bar{y}}{\sqrt{(\Sigma x^2 - n\bar{x}^2)(\Sigma y^2 - n\bar{y}^2)}}.$$

You may use either formulation, since they are algebraically equivalent. Example 4.1, overleaf, gives both methods, so you may judge for yourself.

The quantity, r, provides a standardised measure of correlation. Its value always lies within the range -1 to $+1$. (If you calculate a value outside this range, you have made a mistake.) A value of $+1$ means perfect positive correlation; in this case all the points on a scatter diagram would lie exactly on a straight line with positive gradient. Similarly a value of -1 means perfect negative correlation. These two cases are illustrated in figure 4.9.

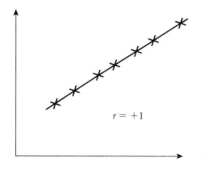
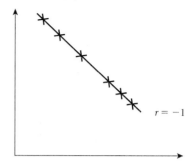

$r = +1$

$r = -1$

Figure 4.9 (i) Perfect positive correlation   **(ii)** Perfect negative correlation

In cases of little or no correlation, r takes values close to zero. The nearer the value of r is to $+1$ or -1, the stronger the correlation.

 Be careful not to confuse the quantities denoted by S_{xx}, S_{yy} and S_{xy} with those denoted by s_{xx}, s_{yy} and s_{xy} and used by some other authors. S_{xx} and S_{yy} are the sums of the squares and are not divided by n. Simlarly, S_{xy} is the sum of the terms $(x_i - \bar{x})(y_i - \bar{y})$ and is not divided by n.

Historical note

Karl Pearson was one of the founders of modern statistics. Born in 1857, he was a man of varied interests and practised law for three years before being appointed Professor of Applied Mathematics and Mechanics at University College, London in 1884. Pearson made contributions to various branches of mathematics but is particularly remembered for his work on the application of statistics to biological problems in heredity and evolution. He died in 1936.

EXAMPLE 4.1

A gardener wishes to know if plants which produce only a few potatoes produce larger ones. He selects five plants at random, sieves out the small potatoes, counts those remaining and weighs the largest one.

Number of potatoes, x	5	5	7	8	10
Weight of largest, y (grams)	240	232	227	222	215

Calculate the sample product moment correlation coefficient, r, and comment on the result.

SOLUTION

Method 1

$n = 5, \bar{x} = 7, \bar{y} = 227.2$

x	y	$x - \bar{x}$	$y - \bar{y}$	$(x - \bar{x})^2$	$(y - \bar{y})^2$	$(x - \bar{x})(y - \bar{y})$
5	240	-2	12.8	4	163.84	-25.6
5	232	-2	4.8	4	23.04	-9.6
7	227	0	-0.2	0	0.04	0
8	222	1	-5.2	1	27.04	-5.2
10	215	3	-12.2	9	148.84	-36.6
35	1136	0	0	18	362.80	-77.0

$$\bar{x} = \frac{\Sigma x}{n} = \frac{35}{5} = 7 \qquad \bar{y} = \frac{\Sigma y}{n} = \frac{1136}{5} = 227.2$$

$\Rightarrow \qquad S_{xx} = \Sigma(x - \bar{x})^2 = 18$

$\Rightarrow \qquad S_{yy} = \Sigma(y - \bar{y})^2 = 362.8$

$\Rightarrow \qquad S_{xy} = \Sigma(x - \bar{x})(y - \bar{y}) = -77$

$\Rightarrow \qquad r = \dfrac{S_{xy}}{\sqrt{S_{xx}S_{yy}}} = \dfrac{\Sigma(x - \bar{x})(y - \bar{y})}{\sqrt{\Sigma(x - \bar{x})^2 \Sigma(y - \bar{y})^2}}$

$$= \frac{-77}{\sqrt{18 \times 362.8}}$$

$$= -0.953 \text{ (to 3 s.f.)}$$

Method 2

$n = 5$

x	y	x^2	y^2	xy
5	240	25	57 600	1200
5	232	25	53 824	1160
7	227	49	51 529	1589
8	222	64	49 284	1776
10	215	100	46 225	2150
35	1136	263	258 462	7875

$$\bar{x} = \frac{\Sigma x}{n} = \frac{35}{5} = 7 \qquad \bar{y} = \frac{\Sigma y}{n} = \frac{1136}{5} = 227.2$$

$$\Rightarrow \qquad S_{xx} = \Sigma x^2 - n\bar{x}^2 = 263 - 5 \times 7^2 = 18$$

$$\Rightarrow \qquad S_{yy} = \Sigma y^2 - n\bar{y}^2 = 258\,462 - 5 \times 227.2^2 = 362.8$$

$$\Rightarrow \qquad S_{xy} = \Sigma xy - n\bar{x}\,\bar{y} = 7875 - 5 \times 7 \times 227.2 = -77$$

$$\Rightarrow \qquad r = \frac{S_{xy}}{\sqrt{S_{xx}S_{yy}}} = \frac{\Sigma xy - n\bar{x}\,\bar{y}}{\sqrt{(\Sigma x^2 - n\bar{x}^2)(\Sigma y^2 - n\bar{y}^2)}}$$

$$= \frac{-77}{\sqrt{18 \times 362.8}}$$

$$= -0.953 \text{ (to 3 s.f.)}$$

Conclusion: There is very strong negative linear correlation between the variables. Large potatoes seem to be associated with small crop sizes.

Notes

- Either method will give the correct value of the product moment correlation coefficient, r.
- Method 2 is generally used when the values of the data give 'awkward' values for the sample means, making the calculations in Method 1 rather unwieldy.
- The 'ingredients' for Method 2 are to be found when using a calculator to find the value of r.

Using a graphic calculator

It is fairly easy to set up a graphic calculator to work out the product moment correlation coefficient and display a scatter diagram. Figure 4.10 shows the output for Example 4.1 obtained by carrying out the following steps.

1 Clear two lists – here list L1 and L2 – and enter the data.
2 Scale both axes.
3 Set up a statistical plot as a scatter diagram, using data from lists L1 and L2.
4 Display the scatter diagram.
5 Display the summary statistics, from which the product moment correlation coefficient, r, may be calculated.
6 Display the product moment correlation coefficient, r, and the coefficients, a and b, of the least squares regression line $y = a + bx$, which you will meet later in this chapter.

Step 1

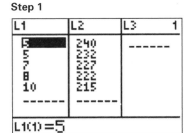

Step 2

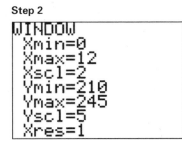

Step 3

Step 4

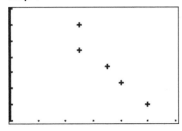

Step 5

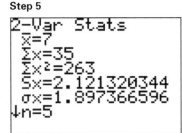

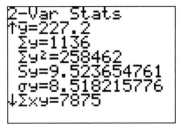

Step 6

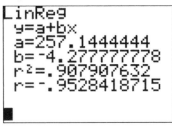

Figure 4.10

The notation used on this calculator display is not quite the same as that used in the books in this series.

- Sx and Sy both refer to standard deviations (divisor $n - 1$).
- σx and σy both refer to root mean square deviations (divisor n).

Note

The illustrations above are taken from a TI-83 graphic calculator. Similar screen shots are possible from other graphic calculators.

Using a spreadsheet

It is also easy to set up a spreadsheet to calculate the product moment correlation coefficient. The spreadsheet in figure 4.11 shows the output for Example 4.1 obtained by carrying out the following steps.

1 Enter the data – here in columns A and B.
2 Use the PEARSON formula from the statistics section – here in cell B11.
3 Highlight the data then use the XY (Scatter) option in the Chartwizard to generate the scatter diagram, customising it as necessary.

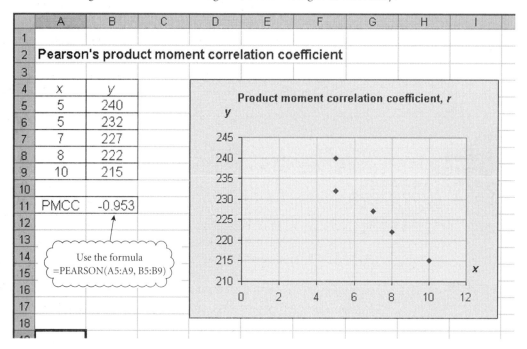

Figure 4.11

1

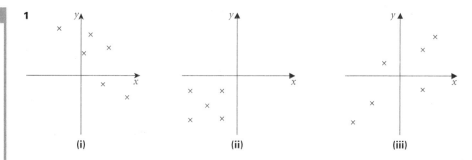

(i)   (ii)   (iii)

Three sets of bivariate data have been plotted on scatter diagrams, as illustrated. In each diagram the product moment correlation coefficient takes one of the values -1, -0.8, 0, 0.8, 1. State the appropriate value of the correlation coefficient corresponding to the scatter diagrams **(i)**, **(ii)** and **(iii)**.

[Cambridge]

2 For each of these sets of data
   (a) draw a scatter diagram and comment on whether there appears to be
        any linear correlation
   (b) calculate the product moment correlation coefficient and compare this
        with your assertion based on the scatter diagram.

   (i) The mathematics and physics test results of 14 students.

Mathematics	45	23	78	91	46	27	41	62	34	17	77	49	55	71
Physics	62	36	92	70	67	39	61	40	55	33	65	59	35	40

   (ii) The wine consumption in a country in millions of litres and the years
        1993 to 2000.

Year	1993	1994	1995	1996	1997	1998	1999	2000
Consumption ($\times 10^6$ litres)	35.5	37.7	41.5	46.4	44.8	45.8	53.9	62.0

   (iii) The number of hours of sunshine and the monthly rainfall, in
        centimetres, in an eight-month period.

	Jan	Feb	Mar	Apr	May	Jun	Jul	Aug
Sunshine (hours)	90	96	105	110	113	120	131	124
Rainfall (cm)	5.1	4.6	6.3	5.1	3.3	2.8	4.5	4.0

   (iv) The annual salary, in thousands of pounds, and the average number of
        hours worked per week by seven people chosen at random.

Salary ($\times$ £1000)	5	7	13	14	16	20	48
Hours worked per week	18	22	35	38	36	36	32

   (v) The mean temperature in degrees celsius and the amount of ice-cream
        sold in a supermarket in hundreds of litres.

	Apr	May	Jun	Jul	Aug	Sep	Oct	Nov
Mean temperature ($^\circ$C)	9	13	14	17	16	15	13	11
Ice-cream sold (100 litres)	11	15	17	20	22	17	8	7

   (vi) The reaction times of eight women of various ages.

Reaction time ($\times 10^{-3}$ s)	156	165	149	180	189	207	208	178
Age (years)	36	40	27	50	49	53	55	27

3 For each of these sets of data use one or more of the following to find the product moment correlation coefficient, r, and plot a scatter diagram.

- a scientific calculator in two variable statistics mode
- a graphic calculator in two variable statistics mode
- a spreadsheet

(i)

x	10	11	12	13	14	15	16	17
y	19	16	28	20	31	19	32	35

(ii)

x	0	1	4	3	2
y	11	8	5	4	7

(iii)

x	12	14	14	15	16	17	17	19
y	86	90	78	71	77	69	80	73

(iv)

x	56	78	14	80	34	78	23	61
y	45	34	67	70	42	18	25	50

The meaning of a sample correlation coefficient

You have already seen that if the value of the correlation coefficient, r, is close to $+1$ or -1, you can be satisfied that there is linear correlation, and that if r is close to 0 there is probably little or no correlation. What happens in a case such as $r = 0.6$?

To answer this question you have to understand what r is actually measuring. The data which you use when calculating r are actually a *sample* of a parent bivariate distribution. You have only taken a few out of a very large number of points which could, in theory, be plotted on a scatter diagram such as figure 4.12. Each point (x_i, y_i) represents one possible value, x_i, of the variable X and one possible value, y_i, of Y.

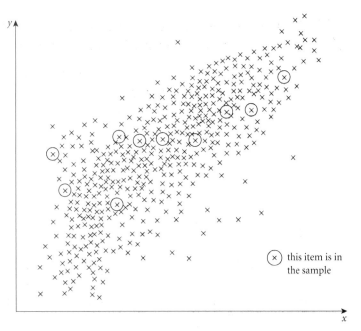

Figure 4.12 Scatter diagram showing a sample from a large bivariate population

There will be a level of correlation within the parent population and this is denoted by ρ (the Greek letter *rho*, pronounced 'row', as in 'row a boat').

The calculated value of r, which is based on the sample points, can be used as an estimate for ρ. It can also be used to carry out a hypothesis test on the value of ρ, the parent population correlation coefficient. Used in this way it is a *test statistic*.

The simplest hypothesis test which you can carry out is that there is no correlation within the parent population. This gives rise to a null hypothesis:

$\quad$ $H_0: \rho = 0$ $\quad$ There is no correlation between the two variables.

There are three possible alternative hypotheses, according to the sense of the situation you are investigating. These are:

1 $H_1: \rho \neq 0$ $\quad$ There is correlation between the variables.
$\qquad\qquad\quad$ (two-tail test)

2 $H_1: \rho > 0$ $\quad$ There is positive correlation between the variables.
$\qquad\qquad\quad$ (one-tail test)

3 $H_1: \rho < 0$ $\quad$ There is negative correlation between the variables.
$\qquad\qquad\quad$ (one-tail test)

The test is carried out by comparing the value for r with the appropriate entry in a table of critical values. This will depend on the size of the sample, the significance level at which you are testing and whether your test is one- or two-tailed.

Critical values

Under the null hypothesis, $H_0: \rho = 0$, i.e. there is a complete absence of linear correlation between the variables in the *population*, it is quite likely that a bivariate data set, drawn at random from the population, will produce a value of r, the *sample* product moment correlation coefficient, which is non-zero.

The role of the significance level is that, for any sample size n, it represents the probability that the value of r will be 'further from zero' than the critical value. Three examples, using the table of critical values in figure 4.13, should help you to understand this concept better.

Alternative hypothesis	Sample size, n	Significance level	Meaning
$H_1: \rho > 0$	11	1%	$P(r > 0.6851) = 0.01$
$H_1: \rho < 0$	6	5%	$P(r < -0.7293) = 0.05$
$H_1: \rho \neq 0$	15	10%	$P(|r| > 0.4409) = 0.1$

EXAMPLE 4.2

THE AVONFORD STAR

Letters to the Editor

Dear Sir,
    The trouble with young people these days is that they watch too much TV. They just sit there gawping and become steadily less intelligent. I challenge you to carry out a proper test and I am sure you will find that the more TV children watch the less intelligent they are.
Yours truly,
Outraged senior citizen.

The editor of *The Avonford Star* was interested in the writer's point of view and managed to collect these data for the IQs of six children, and the number of hours of TV they watched in the previous week.

Hours of TV, x	9	11	14	7	10	9
IQ, y	142	112	100	126	109	88

SOLUTION

The relevant hypothesis test for this situation would be

$H_0: \rho = 0$ There is no correlation between IQ and watching TV.

$H_1: \rho < 0$ There is negative correlation between IQ and watching TV.
        (one-tail test)

The editor decided to use the 5% significance level.

The critical value for $n = 6$ at the 5% significance level for a one-tail test is found from tables to be 0.7293.

	5%	$2\frac{1}{2}$%	1%	$\frac{1}{2}$%	1-tail test
	10%	5%	2%	1%	2-tail-test
n					
1	–	–	–	–	
2	–	–	–	–	
3	0.9877	0.9969	0.9995	0.9999	
4	0.9000	0.9500	0.9800	0.9900	
5	0.8054	0.8783	0.9343	0.9587	
6	0.7293	0.8114	0.8822	0.9172	
7	0.6694	0.7545	0.8329	0.8745	
8	0.6215	0.7067	0.7887	0.8343	
9	0.5822	0.6664	0.7498	0.7977	
10	0.5494	0.6319	0.7155	0.7646	
11	0.5214	0.6021	0.6851	0.7348	
12	0.4973	0.5760	0.6581	0.7079	
13	0.4762	0.5529	0.6339	0.6835	
14	0.4575	0.5324	0.6120	0.6614	
15	0.4409	0.5140	0.5923	0.6411	

Figure 4.13 Extract from table of values for the product moment correlation coefficient, r

The calculation of the product moment correlation coefficient, r, can be set out using *Method 2* from Example 4.1.

$n = 6$

x	y	x^2	y^2	xy
9	142	81	20 164	1278
11	112	121	12 544	1232
14	100	196	10 000	1400
7	126	49	15 876	882
10	109	100	11 881	1090
9	88	81	7 744	792
60	677	628	78 209	6674

$$\bar{x} = \frac{\Sigma x}{n} = \frac{60}{6} = 10 \qquad \bar{y} = \frac{\Sigma y}{n} = \frac{677}{6} = 112.833$$

$$\Rightarrow \qquad S_{xx} = \Sigma x^2 - n\bar{x}^2 = 628 - 6 \times 10^2 = 28$$

$$\Rightarrow \qquad S_{yy} = \Sigma y^2 - n\bar{y}^2 = 78\,209 - 6 \times 112.833\ldots^2 = 1820.833\ldots$$

$$\Rightarrow \qquad S_{xy} = \Sigma xy - n\bar{x}\,\bar{y} = 6674 - 6 \times 10 \times 112.833\ldots = -96$$

$$\Rightarrow \qquad r = \frac{S_{xy}}{\sqrt{S_{xx}S_{yy}}} = \frac{\Sigma xy - n\bar{x}\,\bar{y}}{\sqrt{(\Sigma x^2 - n\bar{x}^2)(\Sigma y^2 - n\bar{y}^2)}} = \frac{-96}{\sqrt{28 \times 1820.833\ldots}}$$

$$= -0.425 \text{ (to 3 s.f.)}$$

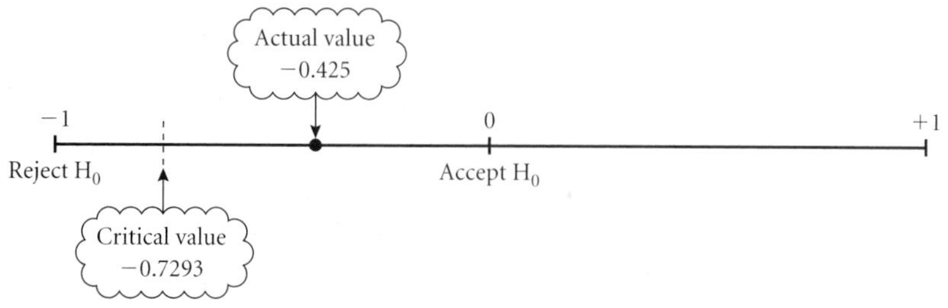

Actual value
−0.425

−1   0   +1

Reject H_0 Accept H_0

Critical value
−0.7293

Figure 4.14

Since $-0.425 > -0.7293$, the critical value at the 5% significance level, the null hypothesis is accepted. (Alternatively, you may use the fact that $0.425 < 0.7293$ to come to the same conclusion.)

The evidence from this small sample is not sufficient to justify the claim that there is negative correlation between IQ and TV watching.

Notice however that, even if it had been, this would not necessarily have supported the Outraged senior citizen's claim that TV lowers IQ. No cause and effect can be implied. It could just be that people with higher IQs watch less TV.

⚠ • Hypothesis tests using Pearson's product moment correlation coefficient require modelling assumptions that both variables are *random* and that the data are drawn from a *bivariate Normal* distribution. For large data sets this is usually the case if the scatter diagram gives an approximately elliptical distribution. If one or both of the distributions is, for example, skewed or bimodal, the procedure is likely to be inaccurate.

• The product moment correlation coefficient is a measure of *linear* correlation. For cases of non-linear association you should apply a test based on Spearman's correlation coefficient, which you will meet later in this chapter.

• The extract from the tables gives the critical value of r for various values of the significance level and the sample size, n. You will, however, find some tables where n is replaced by v, the *degrees of freedom*. Degrees of freedom are covered in the next section.

Degrees of freedom

Here is an example where you have just two data points.

	Sean	Iain
Height of an adult man (m)	1.70	1.90
The mortgage on his house (£)	15 000	45 000

When you plot these two points on a scatter diagram it is possible to join them with a perfect straight line and you might be tempted to conclude that taller men have larger mortgages on their houses.

This conclusion would clearly be wrong. It is based on the data from only two men so you are bound to be able to join the points on the scatter diagram with a straight line and calculate r to be either $+1$ or -1 (providing their heights and/or mortgages are not the same). In order to start to carry out a test you need the data for a third man, say Dafyd (height 1.75 m and mortgage £37 000). When his data are plotted on the scatter diagram in figure 4.15 you can see how close it lies to the line between Sean and Iain.

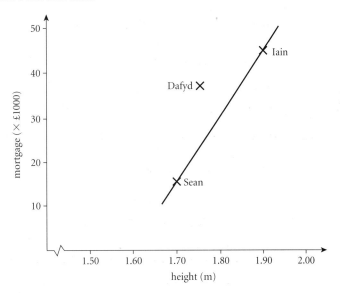

Figure 4.15

So the first two data points do not count towards a test for linear correlation. The first one to count is point number three. Similarly if you have n points, only $n - 2$ of them count towards any test. $n - 2$ is called the *degrees of freedom* and denoted by v. It is the number of free variables in the system. In this case it is the number of points, n, less the 2 that have effectively been used to define the line of best fit.

In the case of the three men with their mortgages you would actually draw a line of best fit through all three, rather than join any particular two. So you cannot say that any two particular points have been taken out to draw the line of best fit, merely that the system as a whole has lost two.

Tables of critical values of correlation coefficients can be used without understanding the idea of degrees of freedom, but the idea is an important one which you will often use as you learn more statistics. In general

$$\text{degrees of freedom} = \text{sample size} - \text{number of restrictions}.$$

Different types of restriction apply in different statistical procedures.

Interpreting correlation

You need to be on your guard against drawing spurious conclusions from significant correlation coefficients.

Correlation does not imply causation

Figures for the years 1985–93 show a high correlation between the sales of personal computers and those of microwave ovens. There is of course no direct connection between the two variables. You would be quite wrong to conclude that buying a microwave oven predisposes you to buy a computer as well, or vice versa.

Although there may be a high level of correlation between variables A and B it does not mean that A causes B or that B causes A. It may well be that a third variable C causes both A and B, or it may be that there is a more complicated set of relationships. In the case of personal computers and microwaves, both are clearly caused by the advance of modern technology.

Non-linear correlation

A low value of r tells you that there is little or no *linear* correlation. There are, however, other forms of correlation, as illustrated in figure 4.16.

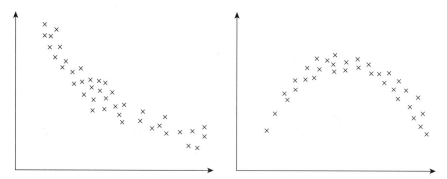

Figure 4.16 Scatter diagrams showing non-linear correlation

These diagrams show that there is an association between the variables, but not one of linear correlation.

Extrapolation

A linear relationship established over a particular domain should not be assumed to hold outside this range. For instance, there is strong correlation between the age in years and the 100-metre times of female athletes between the ages of 10 and 20 years. To extend the connection, as shown in figure 4.17, would suggest that veteran athletes are quicker than athletes who are in their prime and, if they live long enough, can even run 100 metres in no time at all!

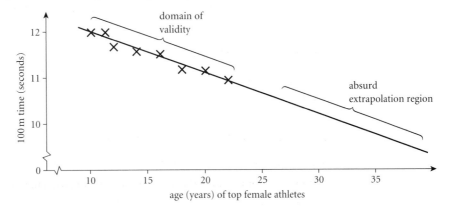

Figure 4.17

Most of the questions in this exercise involve unrealistically small samples. They are meant to help you understand the principles involved in testing for correlation. When you come to do such testing on real data, you would hope to be able to use much larger samples.

1   A language teacher wishes to test whether students who are good at their own language are also likely to be good at a foreign language. Accordingly she collects the marks of eight students, all native English speakers, in their end of year examinations in English and French.

Candidate	A	B	C	D	E	F	G	H
English	65	34	48	72	58	63	26	80
French	74	49	45	80	63	72	12	75

(i)   Calculate the product moment correlation coefficient.

(ii)   State the null and alternative hypotheses.

(iii)   Using the correlation coefficient as a test statistic, carry out the test at the 5% significance level.

2 'You can't win without scoring goals.' So says the coach of a netball team. Jamila, who believes in solid defensive play, disagrees and sets out to prove that there is no correlation between scoring goals and winning matches. She collects the following data for the goals scored and the points gained by 12 teams in a netball league.

Goals scored, x	41	50	54	47	47	49	52	61	50	29	47	35
Points gained, y	21	20	19	18	16	14	12	11	11	7	5	2

(i) Calculate the product moment correlation coefficient.
(ii) State suitable null and alternative hypotheses, indicating whose position each represents.
(iii) Carry out the hypothesis test at the 5% significance level and comment on the result.

3 A sports reporter believes that those who are good at the high jump are also good at the long jump, and vice versa. He collects data on the best performances of nine athletes, as follows.

Athlete	A	B	C	D	E	F	G	H	I
High jump, x (metres)	2.0	2.1	1.8	2.1	1.8	1.9	1.6	1.8	1.8
Long jump, y (metres)	8.0	7.6	6.4	6.8	5.8	8.0	5.5	5.5	6.6

(i) Calculate the product moment correlation coefficient.
(ii) State suitable null and alternative hypotheses.
(iii) Carry out the hypothesis test at the 5% significance level and comment on the result.

4 It is widely believed that those who are good at chess are good at bridge, and vice versa. A commentator decides to test this theory using as data the grades of a random sample of eight people who play both games.

Player	A	B	C	D	E	F	G	H
Chess grade	160	187	129	162	149	151	189	158
Bridge grade	75	100	75	85	80	70	95	80

(i) Calculate the product moment correlation coefficient.
(ii) State suitable null and alternative hypotheses.
(iii) Carry out the hypothesis test at the 5% significance level. Do these data support this belief at this significance level?

5 A biologist believes that a particular type of fish develops black spots on its scales in water that is polluted by certain agricultural fertilisers. She catches a number of fish; for each one she counts the number of black spots on its scales and measures the concentration of the pollutant in the water it was swimming in. She uses these data to test for positive linear correlation between the number of spots and the level of pollution.

Fish	A	B	C	D	E	F	G	H	I	J
Pollutant concentration (parts per million)	124	59	78	79	150	12	23	45	91	68
Number of black spots	15	8	7	8	14	0	4	5	8	8

(i) Calculate the product moment correlation coefficient.
(ii) State suitable null and alternative hypotheses.
(iii) Carry out the hypothesis test at the 2% significance level. What can the biologist conclude?

6 Andrew claims that the older you get, the slower is your reaction time. His mother disagrees, saying the two are unrelated. They decide that the only way to settle the discussion is to carry out a proper test. A few days later they are having a small party and so ask their twelve guests to take a test that measures their reaction times. The results are as follows.

Age	Reaction time (s)	Age	Reaction time (s)
78	0.8	35	0.5
72	0.6	30	0.3
60	0.7	28	0.4
56	0.5	20	0.4
41	0.5	19	0.3
39	0.4	10	0.3

Carry out the test at the 5% significance level, stating the null and alternative hypotheses. Who won the argument, Andrew or his mother?

7 The teachers at a school have a discussion as to whether girls in general run faster or slower as they get older. They decide to collect data for a random sample of girls the next time the school cross country race is held (which everybody has to take part in). They collect the following data, with the times given in minutes and the ages in years (the conversion from months to decimal parts of a year has already been carried out).

Age	Time	Age	Time	Age	Time
11.6	23.1	18.2	45.0	13.9	29.1
15.0	24.0	15.4	23.2	18.1	21.2
18.8	45.0	14.4	26.1	13.4	23.9
16.0	25.2	16.1	29.4	16.2	26.0
12.8	26.4	14.6	28.1	17.5	23.4
17.6	22.9	18.7	45.0	17.0	25.0
17.4	27.1	15.4	27.0	12.5	26.3
13.2	25.2	11.8	25.4	12.7	24.2
14.5	26.8				

(i) State suitable null and alternative hypotheses and decide on an appropriate significance level for the test.

(ii) Calculate the product moment correlation coefficient and state the conclusion from the test.

(iii) Plot the data on a scatter diagram and identify any outliers. Explain how they could have arisen.

(iv) Comment on the validity of the test.

8 The manager of a company wishes to evaluate the success of its training programme. One aspect which interests her is to see if there is any relationship between the amount of training given to employees and the length of time they stay with the company before moving on to jobs elsewhere. She does not want to waste company money training people who will shortly leave. At the same time she believes that the more training employees are given, the longer they will stay. She collects data on the average number of days training given per year to 25 employees who have recently left for other jobs, and the length of time they worked for the company.

Training (days/year)	Work (days)	Training (days/year)	Work (days)	Training (days/year)	Work (days)
2.0	354	3.4	760	1.2	132
4.0	820	1.8	125	4.5	1365
0.1	78	0.0	28	1.0	52
5.6	1480	5.7	1360	7.8	1080
9.1	980	7.2	1520	3.7	508
2.6	902	7.5	1380	10.9	1281
0.0	134	3.0	121	3.8	945
2.6	252	2.8	457	2.9	692
7.2	867				

(i) Calculate the product moment correlation coefficient.

(ii) State suitable null and alternative hypotheses.

(iii) Carry out the hypothesis test at the 5% significance level.

(iv) Plot the data on a scatter diagram.

(v) What conclusions would you come to if you were the manager?

9 Charlotte is a campaigner for temperance, believing that drinking alchohol is an evil habit. Michel, a representative of a wine company, presents her with these figures which he claims show that wine drinking is good for marriages.

Country	Wine consumption (litres/person/year)	Divorce rate (per 1000 inhabitants)
Belgium	20	2.0
Denmark	20	2.7
Germany	26	2.2
Greece	33	0.6
Italy	63	0.4
Portugal	54	0.9
Spain	41	0.6
U.K.	13	2.9

(i) Write Michel's claim in the form of a hypothesis test and carry it out.

(ii) Charlotte claims that Michel is 'indulging in pseudo-statistics'. What arguments could she use to support this point of view?

10 The values of x and y in the table are the marks obtained in an intelligence test and a university examination, respectively, by 20 medical students. The data are plotted in the scatter diagram.

x	98	51	71	57	44	59	75	47	39	58
y	85	40	30	25	50	40	50	35	25	90
x	77	65	58	66	79	72	45	40	49	76
y	65	25	70	45	70	50	40	20	30	60

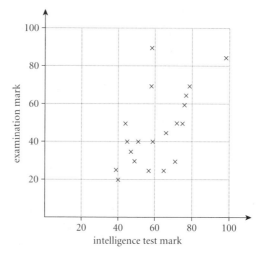

Given that $\Sigma x = 1226$, $\Sigma y = 945$, $\Sigma x^2 = 79\,732$, $\Sigma y^2 = 52\,575$ and $\Sigma xy = 61\,495$, calculate the product moment correlation coefficient, r, to 2 decimal places.

Referring to the evidence provided by the diagram and the value of r, comment briefly on the correlation between the two sets of marks.

Now eliminate from consideration those 10 students whose values of x are less than 50 or more than 75. Calculate the new value of r for the marks of the remaining students. What does the comparison with the earlier value of r seem to indicate?

[MEI]

11 A random sample of students who are shortly to sit an examination are asked to keep a record of how long they spend revising, in order to investigate whether more revision time is associated with a higher mark. The data are given below, with x hours being the revision time (correct to the nearest half hour) and $y\%$ being the mark scored in the examination.

x	0	3	4.5	3.5	7	5.5	5	6.5	6	10.5	2
y	36	52	52	57	60	61	63	63	64	70	89

(i) Obtain the value of the product moment correlation coefficient for the data.

(ii) Specify appropriate null and alternative hypotheses, and carry out a suitable test at the 5% level of significance.

(iii) Without further calculation, state the effect of the data $x = 2$, $y = 89$ on the value of the product moment correlation coefficient. Explain whether or not this point should be excluded when carrying out the hypothesis test.

[MEI]

12 In order to investigate the strength of the correlation between the value of a house and the value of the householder's car, a random sample of householders was questioned. The resulting data are shown in the table, the units being thousands of pounds.

x	110	106	51	94	66	26	72	51	53	133
y	12	9.5	2.4	4.2	4.1	0.3	3.2	6.0	7.8	15

(i) Represent the data graphically.

(ii) Calculate the product moment correlation coefficient.

(iii) Carry out a suitable hypothesis test, at a suitable level of significance, to determine whether or not it is reasonable to suppose that the value of a house is positively correlated with the value of the householder's car.

(iv) A student argues that when two variables are correlated one must be the cause of the other. Briefly discuss this view with regard to the data in this question.

[MEI]

Rank correlation

THE AVONFORD STAR

Punch-up at the village fete

Pandemonium broke out at the Normanton village fete last Saturday when the adjudication for the Tomato of the Year competition was announced. The two judges completely failed to agree in their rankings and so a compromise winner was chosen to the fury of everybody (except the winner).

Following the announcement there was a moment of stunned silence, followed by shouts of 'Rubbish', 'It's a fix', 'Go home' and further abuse. Then the tomatoes started to fly and before long fighting broke out.

By the time police arrived on the scene ten people were injured, including last year's winner Bert Wallis who lost three teeth in the scrap. Both judges had escaped unhurt.

Angry Bert Wallis, nursing a badly bruised jaw, said 'The competition was a nonsense. The judges were useless. Their failure to agree shows that they did not know what they were looking for'. But fete organiser Margaret Bramble said this was untrue. 'The competition was completely fair; both judges know a good tomato when they see one,' she claimed.

The judgement that caused all the trouble was as follows.

Tomato	A	B	C	D	E	F	G	H
Judge 1	1	8	4	6	2	5	7	3
Judge 2	7	2	3	4	6	8	1	5
Total	8	10	(7)	10	8	13	8	8

Winner

You will see that both judges ranked the eight entrants, 1st, 2nd, 3rd, ..., 8th. The winner, C, was placed 4th by one judge and 3rd by the other. Their rankings look different so perhaps they were using different criteria on which to assess them. How can you use these data to decide whether that was or was not the case?

One way would be to calculate a correlation coefficient and use it to carry out a hypothesis test:

$H_0: \rho = 0$ There is no correlation.
$H_1: \rho > 0$ There is positive correlation.

The null hypothesis, H_0, represents something like Bert Wallis's view, the alternative hypothesis that of Margaret Bramble.

However, the data you have are of a different type from any that you have used before for calculating correlation coefficients. In the point $(1, 7)$, corresponding to tomato A, the numbers 1 and 7 are *ranks* and not scores (like marks in an examination or measurements). It is, however, possible to calculate a *rank correlation coefficient*, and in the same way as before.

Tomato	Judge 1 x	Judge 2 y	x^2	y^2	xy
A	1	7	1	49	7
B	8	2	64	4	16
C	4	3	16	9	12
D	6	4	36	16	24
E	2	6	4	36	12
F	5	8	25	64	40
G	7	1	49	1	7
H	3	5	9	25	15
Total	36	36	204	204	133

$$\bar{x} = \frac{\Sigma x}{n} = \frac{36}{8} = 4.5 \qquad \text{Similarly } \bar{y} = \frac{\Sigma y}{n} = \frac{36}{8} = 4.5$$

$$\Rightarrow \qquad S_{xx} = \Sigma x^2 - n\bar{x}^2 = 204 - 8 \times 4.5^2 = 42$$

$$\Rightarrow \qquad S_{yy} = \Sigma y^2 - n\bar{y}^2 = 204 - 8 \times 4.5^2 = 42$$

$$\Rightarrow \qquad S_{xy} = \Sigma xy - n\bar{x}\,\bar{y} = 133 - 8 \times 4.5^2 = -29$$

$$\Rightarrow \qquad r = \frac{S_{xy}}{\sqrt{S_{xx}S_{yy}}}$$

$$= \frac{-29}{\sqrt{42 \times 42}}$$

$$= -0.690 \text{ (to 3 s.f)}$$

Since the correlation coefficient is negative there can be no possibility of accepting H_1, therefore you accept H_0. There is no evidence of agreement between the judges. Remember this was a one-tail test for positive correlation.

Spearman's coefficient of rank correlation

The calculation in the previous example is usually carried out by a quite different, but equivalent, procedure and the resulting correlation coefficient is called *Spearman's coefficient of rank correlation* and denoted by r_s.

The procedure is summarised by the formula

$$r_s = 1 - \frac{6\Sigma d_i^2}{n(n^2 - 1)}$$

where d_i is the difference in the ranks given to the ith item.

The calculation is then as follows.

Tomato	Judge 1 x_i	Judge 2 y_i	$d_i = x_i - y_i$	d_i^2
A	1	7	-6	36
B	8	2	6	36
C	4	3	1	1
D	6	4	2	4
E	2	6	-4	16
F	5	8	-3	9
G	7	1	6	36
H	3	5	-2	4
Total				142

$$r_s = 1 - \frac{6\Sigma d_i^2}{n(n^2 - 1)} = 1 - \frac{6 \times 142}{8(8^2 - 1)}$$

$$= 1 - 1.690$$

$$= -0.690 \text{ (to 3 s.f.)}$$

You will see that this is the same answer as before, but the working is much shorter. It is not difficult to prove that the two methods are equivalent and this is done in Appendix 3.

Critical values for Spearman's rank correlation coefficient, however, are different from those for Pearson's product moment correlation coefficient, so you must always be careful to use the appropriate tables.

The calculation is often carried out with the data across the page rather than in columns and this is shown in the next example.

EXAMPLE 4.3

During their course two trainee tennis coaches, Rachael and Leroy, were shown videos of seven people, A, B, C, . . ., G, doing a top-spin service and were asked to rank them in order according to the quality of their style. They placed them as follows.

Rank order	1	2	3	4	5	6	7
Rachael	B	G	F	D	A	C	E
Leroy	F	B	D	E	G	A	C

(i) Find Spearman's coefficient of rank correlation.
(ii) Use it to test whether there is evidence, at the 5% level, of positive correlation between their judgements.

SOLUTION

(i) The rankings are as follows.

Person	A	B	C	D	E	F	G
Rachael	5	1	6	4	7	3	2
Leroy	6	2	7	3	4	1	5
d_i	-1	-1	-1	1	3	2	-3
d_i^2	1	1	1	1	9	4	9

$$n = 7 \qquad \Sigma d_i^2 = 26$$

$$r_s = 1 - \frac{6\Sigma d_i^2}{n(n^2 - 1)} = 1 - \frac{6 \times 26}{7(7^2 - 1)}$$

$$= 0.54 \qquad \text{(2 d.p.)}$$

(ii) $H_0: \rho = 0$ There is no correlation between their rankings.

$H_1: \rho > 0$ There is positive correlation between their rankings.

Significance level 5%, one-tail test.

From tables, the critical value of r_s for a one-tail test at this significance level for $n = 7$ is 0.7143.

$0.54 < 0.7143$ so H_0 is accepted.

	5%	$2\frac{1}{2}\%$	1%	$\frac{1}{2}\%$	1-tail test
	10%	5%	2%	1%	2-tail-test
n					
1	–	–	–	–	
2	–	–	–	–	
3	–	–	–	–	
4	1.0000	–	–	–	
5	0.9000	1.0000	1.0000	–	
6	0.8286	0.8857	0.9429	1.0000	
7	0.7143	0.7857	0.8929	0.9286	
8	0.6429	0.7381	0.8333	0.8810	
9	0.6000	0.7000	0.7833	0.8333	
10	0.5636	0.6485	0.7455	0.7939	

Figure 4.18 Extract from table of critical values for Spearman's rank correlation coefficient, r_s

There is insufficient evidence to claim positive correlation between Rachael's and Leroy's rankings.

Historical note

Charles Spearman was born in London in 1863. After serving 14 years in the army as a cavalry officer, he went to Leipzig to study psychology. On completing his doctorate there he became a lecturer, and soon afterwards a professor, at University College, London. He pioneered the application of statistical techniques within psychology and developed the technique known as factor analysis in order to analyse different aspects of human ability. He died in 1945.

Tied ranks

If several items are ranked equally you give them the mean of the ranks they would have had if they had been slightly different from each other.

For example A, B, . . ., J are ranked.

1	2=	2=	4	5	6=	6=	6=	9	10
C	G	J	A	D	B	I	F	E	H

G and J are both 2= and so are given the rank $\dfrac{2+3}{2} = 2.5$.

B, I and F are all 6= and so are given the rank $\dfrac{6+7+8}{3} = 7$.

When to use rank correlation

Sometimes your data will be available in two forms, as values of variables or in rank order. If you have the choice you will usually work out the correlation coefficient from the variable values rather than the ranks.

It may well be the case, however, that only ranked data are available to you and in that case you have no choice but to use them. It may also be that, while you could collect variable values as well, it would not be worth the time, trouble or expense to do so.

Pearson's product moment correlation coefficient is a measure of *linear* correlation and so is not appropriate for non-linear data like those illustrated in the scatter diagram in figure 4.19. You may, however, use rank correlation to investigate whether one variable generally increases (or decreases) as the other increases.

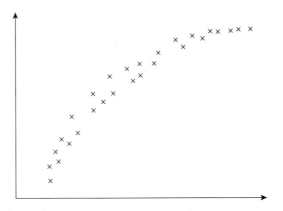

Figure 4.19 Non-linear data with a high degree of rank correlation

You should, however, always look at the sense of your data before deciding which is the more appropriate form of correlation to use.

Note

Spearman's rank correlation coefficient provides one among many statistical tests that can be carried out on ranks rather than variable values. Such tests are examples of *non-parametric tests*. A non-parametric test is a test on some aspect of a distribution which is not specified by its defining parameters.

1 The order of merit of ten individuals at the start and finish of a training course were as follows.

Individual	A	B	C	D	E	F	G	H	I	J
Order at start	1	2	3	4	5	6	7	8	9	10
Order at finish	5	3	1	9	2	6	4	7	10	8

Find Spearman's coefficient of rank correlation between the two orders.

2 A psychologist obtained scores by nine university entrants in three tests (A, B and C). The scores in tests A and B were as follows.

Entrant	1	2	3	4	5	6	7	8	9
A score	8	3	9	10	4	9	6	4	5
B score	7	8	5	9	10	6	3	4	7

Calculate a coefficient of rank correlation between the two sets of scores. The coefficient obtained between the A and C scores was 0.71 and that between the B and C scores was 0.62. What advice would you give the psychologist if he wished to use fewer than three tests?

[Cambridge]

3 In a driving competition there were eight contestants and three judges who placed them in rank order as shown in the table below.

Competitor	A	B	C	D	E	F	G	H
Judge X	2	5	6	1	8	4	7	3
Judge Y	1	6	8	3	7	2	4	5
Judge Z	2=	2=	6=	4	6=	1	6=	5

(i) Which two judges agreed the most?

(ii) Stating suitable null and alternative hypotheses, carry out a hypothesis test on the level of agreement of these two judges.

4 A coach wanted to test his theory that, although athletes have specialisms, it is still true that those who run fast at one distance are also likely to run fast at another distance. He selected six athletes at random to take part in a test and invited them to compete over 100 m and over 1500 m.

The times and places of the six athletes were as follows.

Athlete	100 m time	100 m rank	1500 m time	1500 m rank
Allotey	9.8 s	1	3 m 42 s	1
Chell	10.9 s	6	4 m 11 s	2
Giles	10.4 s	2	4 m 19 s	6
Mason	10.5 s	3	4 m 18 s	5
O'Hara	10.7 s	5	4 m 12 s	3
Stuart	10.6 s	4	4 m 16 s	4

(i) Calculate the Pearson product moment and Spearman's rank correlation coefficients for these data.

(ii) State suitable null and alternative hypotheses and carry out hypothesis tests on these data.

(iii) State which you consider to be the more appropriate correlation coefficient in this situation, giving your reasons.

5 At the end of a word-processing course the trainees are given a document to type. They are assessed on the time taken and on the quality of their work. For a random sample of 12 trainees the following results were obtained.

Trainee	A	B	C	D	E	F	G	H	I	J	K	L
Quality (%)	97	96	94	91	90	87	86	83	82	80	77	71
Time (s)	210	230	198	204	213	206	200	186	192	202	191	199

(i) Calculate Spearman's coefficient of rank correlation for the data. Explain what the sign of your correlation coefficient indicates about the data.

(ii) Carry out a test, at the 5% level of significance, of whether or not there is any correlation between time taken and quality of work for trainees who have attended this word-processing course. State clearly the null and alternative hypotheses under test and the conclusion reached.

[MEI]

6 A school holds an election for parent governors. Candidates are invited to write brief autobiographies and these are sent out at the same time as the voting papers.

After the election, one of the candidates, Mr Smith, says that the more words you wrote about yourself the more votes you got. He sets out to 'prove this statistically' by calculating the product moment correlation between the number of words and the number of votes.

Candidate	A	B	C	D	E	F	G
Number of words	70	101	106	232	150	102	98
Number of votes	99	108	97	144	94	54	87

(i) Calculate the product moment correlation coefficient.

Mr Smith claims that this proves his point at the 5% significance level.

(ii) State his null and alternative hypotheses and show how he came to his conclusion.

(iii) Calculate Spearman's rank correlation coefficient for these data.

(iv) Explain the difference in the two correlation coefficients and criticise the procedure Mr Smith used in coming to his conclusion.

7 To test the belief that milder winters are followed by warmer summers, meteorological records are obtained for a random sample of ten years. For each year the mean temperatures are found for January and July. The data, in degrees Celsius, are given below.

January	8.3	7.1	9.0	1.8	3.5	4.7	5.8	6.0	2.7	2.1
July	16.2	13.1	16.7	11.2	14.9	15.1	17.7	17.3	12.3	13.4

(i) Rank the data and calculate Spearman's rank correlation coefficient.

(ii) Test, at the 2.5% level of significance, the belief that milder winters are followed by warmer summers. State clearly the null and alternative hypotheses under test.

(iii) Would it be more appropriate, less appropriate or equally appropriate to use the product moment correlation coefficient to analyse these data? Briefly explain why.

[MEI]

8 The following data, referring to the ordering of perceived risk of 25 activities and technologies and actual fatality estimates, were obtained in a study in the United States. Use these data to test at the 5% significance level for positive correlation between

(i) the League of Women Voters and college students

(ii) experts and actual fatality estimates

(iii) college students and experts.

Comment on your results and identify any outliers in the three sets of bivariate data you have just used.

	League of Women Voters	College students	Experts	Actual fatalaties (estimates)
Nuclear power	1	1	18	16
Motor vehicles	2	4	1	3
Handguns	3	2	4	4
Smoking	4	3	2	1
Motorcycles	5	5	6	6
Alcoholic beverages	6	6	3	2
General (private) aviation	7	12	11	11
Police work	8	7	15	18
Surgery	9	10	5	8
Fire fighting	10	9	16	17
Large construction	11	11	12	12
Hunting	12	15	20	14
Mountain climbing	13	17	24	21
Bicycles	14	19	13	13
Commercial aviation	15	13	14	20
Electric power (non-nuclear)	16	16	8	5
Swimming	17	25	9	7
Contraceptives	18	8	10	19
Skiing	19	20	25	24
X-rays	20	14	7	9
High school & college football	21	21	22	23
Railroads	22	18	17	10
Power mowers	23	23	23	22
Home appliances	24	22	19	15
Vaccinations	25	24	21	25

Source: Shwing and Albers, *Societal Risk Assessment*, Plenum

9 In a random sample of eight areas, residents were asked to express their approval or disapproval of the services provided by the local authority. A score of zero represented complete dissatisfaction, and ten represented complete satisfaction. The table below shows the mean score for each local authority together with the authority's level of community charge.

Authority	A	B	C	D	E	F	G	H
Community charge (£)	485	490	378	451	384	352	420	212
Approval rating	3.0	4.0	5.0	4.6	4.1	5.5	5.8	6.1

(i) Calculate Spearman's rank correlation coefficient for the data.

(ii) Carry out a significance test at the 5% level using the value of the correlation coefficient which you have calculated. State carefully the null and alternative hypotheses under test and the conclusion to be drawn.

[MEI]

10 A fertiliser additive is claimed to enhance the growth of marrows. To test the claim statistically, a random sample of ten marrows is treated with varying levels of additive. The amounts of additive (in ounces) and the eventual weights of the marrows (in pounds) are given in the table.

Amount of additive	8.2	3.5	8.8	1.6	1.9	9.9	5.8	5.5	4.4	3.9
Weight of marrow	6.6	7.2	8.4	4.7	7.4	8.7	7.5	7.3	5.9	7.0

(i) Rank the data and calculate Spearman's coefficient of rank correlation.

(ii) State appropriate null and alternative hypotheses for the test. Justify the alternative hypothesis you have given.

(iii) Carry out the test using a 5% level of significance. State clearly the conclusion reached.

(iv) Suppose it is discovered that the figures for the amounts of additive shown in the table were weights in grams rather than ounces. State, with reasons, whether this does or does not invalidate your answer.

[MEI]

11 In order to assess whether increased expenditure in schools produces better examination results, a survey of all the secondary schools in England was conducted. Data on a random sample of 12 of these schools are shown below. The score shown is a measure of academic performance, a higher score indicating a higher success rate in examinations; expenditure is measured in thousands of pounds per student per year.

Score	1.54	1.50	1.49	1.22	1.19	1.11	1.09	1.06	1.05	0.97	0.88	0.68
Expenditure	1.70	3.95	2.75	1.95	2.35	1.45	2.40	2.05	2.15	2.30	1.75	2.10

(i) Calculate the value of Spearman's rank correlation coefficient for the data.

(ii) Perform an appropriate test at the 5% level, making clear what your hypotheses are. State clearly the conclusions to be drawn from the test.

Now suppose that the value of Spearman's rank correlation coefficient, calculated for *all* the secondary schools in England, is 0.15.

(iii) What conclusion would you now reach about any association between expenditure per student and examination success, and why?

[**MEI**]

12 In a national survey into whether low death rates are associated with greater prosperity, a random sample of 14 areas was taken. The areas, arranged in order of their prosperity, are shown in the table below together with their death rates. (The death rates are on a scale for which 100 is the national average.)

most prosperous   least prosperous

Area	A	B	C	D	E	F	G	H	I	J	K	L	M	N
Death rate	66	76	84	83	102	78	100	110	105	112	122	131	165	138

(i) Calculate an appropriate correlation coefficient and use it to test, at the 5% level of significance, whether or not there is such an association. State your hypotheses and your conclusion carefully.

(ii) A newspaper carried this story under the headline 'Poverty causes increased deaths'. Explain carefully whether or not the data justify this headline.

(iii) The data include no information on the age distributions in the different areas. Explain why such additional information would be relevant.

[**MEI**]

The least squares regression line

A correlation coefficient provides you with a measure of the level of association between the two variables in a bivariate distribution.

If this indicates that there is a relationship, your question will be 'What is it?' In the case of linear correlation it can be expressed algebraically as a linear equation or geometrically as a straight line on the scatter diagram.

Before you do any calculations you first need to look carefully at the two variables that give rise to your data. It is normal practice to plot the *dependent variable* on the vertical axis and the *independent variable* on the horizontal axis. In the example which follows, the independent variable is the time at which measurements are made. (Notice that this is a non-random variable.) The procedure leads to the equation of the *regression line*, the line of best fit in these circumstances.

Look at the scatter diagram (figure 4.20) showing the n points $A(x_1, y_1)$, $B(x_2, y_2)$, ..., $N(x_n, y_n)$. On it is marked a possible line of best fit ℓ. If the line ℓ

passed through all the points there would be no problem since there would be perfect linear correlation. It does not, of course, pass though all the points and you would be very surprised if such a line did in any real situation.

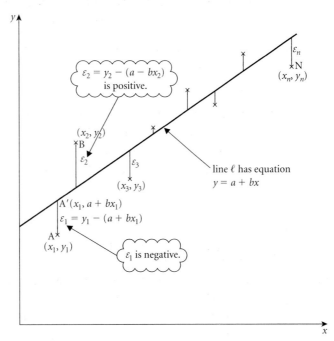

Figure 4.20 Bivariate data plotted on a scatter diagram with the regression line, ℓ, $y = a + bx$, and the residuals ε_1, ε_2, ..., ε_n

By how much is it missing the points? The answer to that question is shown by the vertical lines from the points to the line. Their lengths ε_1, ε_2, ..., ε_n are called the *residuals* and represent the variation which is not explained by the line ℓ. The *least squares regression line* is the line which produces the least possible value of the sum of the squares of the residuals, $\varepsilon_1^2 + \varepsilon_2^2 + \ldots + \varepsilon_n^2$.

If the equation of the line ℓ is $y = a + bx$, then it is easy to see that the point A′ on the diagram, directly above A, has co-ordinates $(x_1, a + bx_1)$ and so the corresponding residual, ε_1, is given by $\varepsilon_1 = y_1 - (a + bx_1)$. Similarly for $\varepsilon_2, \varepsilon_3, \ldots, \varepsilon_n$.

The problem is to find the values of the constants a and b in the equation of the line ℓ which make $\varepsilon_1^2 + \varepsilon_2^2 + \ldots + \varepsilon_n^2$ a minimum for any particular set of data, that is to minimise

$$[y_1 - (a + bx_1)]^2 + [y_2 - (a + bx_2)]^2 + \ldots + [y_n - (a + bx_n)]^2$$

The mathematics involved in doing this is not particularly difficult and is given in Appendix 4. The resulting equation of the regression line is

$$y - \bar{y} = \frac{S_{xy}}{S_{xx}} (x - \bar{x}).$$

There are a number of equivalent ways of writing S_{xx} and S_{xy}.

Notes

1 In the preceding work you will see that only variation in the *y* values has been considered. The reason for this is that the *x* values represent a non-random variable. That is why the residuals are vertical and not in any other direction. Thus $y_1, y_2, \ldots$ are values of a random variable *Y* given by $Y = a + bx + \varepsilon$ where ε is the residual variation, the variation that is not explained by the regression line.

2 The goodness of fit of a regression line may be judged by eye by looking at a scatter diagram. An informal measure which is often used is the coefficient of determination, r^2, which measures the proportion of the total variation in the dependent variable, *Y*, which is accounted for by the regression line. There is no standard hypothesis test based on the coefficient of determination.

3 This form of the regression line is often called the *y on x regression line*. If for some reason you had *y* as your independent variable, you would use the '*x* on *y*' form obtained by interchanging *x* and *y* in the equation.

4 Although the derivation given in Appendix 4 is only true for a random variable on a non-random variable, it happens that, for quite different reasons, the same form of the regression line applies if both variables are random and Normally distributed. If this is the case the scatter diagram will usually show an approximately elliptical distribution. Since this is a common situation, this form of the regression line may be used more widely than might at first have seemed to be the case.

EXAMPLE 4.4

A patient is given a drip feed containing a particular chemical and its concentration in his blood is measured, in suitable units, at one hour intervals for the next five hours. The doctors believe the figures to be subject to random errors, arising both from the sampling procedure and the subsequent chemical analysis, but that a linear model is appropriate.

Time, *x* (hours)	0	1	2	3	4	5
Concentration, *y*	2.4	4.3	5.2	6.8	9.1	11.8

(i) Find the equation of the regression line of *y* on *x*.

(ii) Illustrate the data and your regression line on a scatter diagram.

(iii) Estimate the concentration of the chemical in the patient's blood

   (a) $3\frac{1}{2}$ hours   (b) 10 hours

   after treatment started.

   Comment on the likely accuracy of your predictions.

(iv) Calculate the residuals for each data pair. Mark them on your scatter diagram. Check that the sum of the residuals is zero and find the sum of the squares of the residuals.

SOLUTION

(i) You can adapt *Method 2* from Example 4.1 on correlation analysis.

$n = 6$

x	y	x^2	xy
0	2.4	0	0.0
1	4.3	1	4.3
2	5.2	4	10.4
3	6.8	9	20.4
4	9.1	16	36.4
5	11.8	25	59.0
15	39.6	55	130.5

$$\bar{x} = \frac{\Sigma x}{n} = \frac{15}{6} = 2.5 \qquad \bar{y} = \frac{\Sigma y}{n} = \frac{39.6}{6} = 6.6$$

$\Rightarrow \qquad S_{xx} = \Sigma x^2 - n\bar{x}^2 = 55 - 6 \times 2.5^2 = 17.5$

$\Rightarrow \qquad S_{xy} = \Sigma xy - n\bar{x}\,\bar{y} = 130.5 - 6 \times 2.5 \times 6.6 = 31.5$

$\Rightarrow \qquad b = \frac{S_{xy}}{S_{xx}} = \frac{\Sigma xy - n\bar{x}\,\bar{y}}{\Sigma x^2 - n\bar{x}^2} = \frac{31.5}{17.5} = 1.8$

Hence the least squares regression line is given by

$$y - \bar{y} = b(x - \bar{x})$$

$\Rightarrow \qquad y - 6.6 = 1.8(x - 2.5)$

$\Rightarrow \qquad y = 2.1 + 1.8x$

(ii)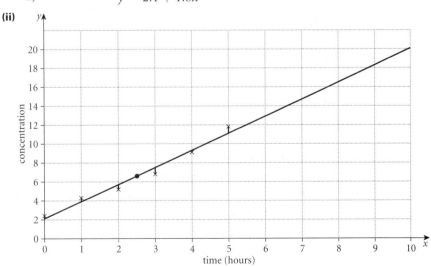

Figure 4.21

(iii) When $x = 3.5$,

$$y = 2.1 + 1.8 \times 3.5$$
$$= 8.4.$$

The concentration of 8.4 lies between the measured values of 6.8 at time 3 hours and 9.1 at time 4 hours, so the prediction seems quite reasonable.

When $x = 10$,

$$y = 2.1 + 1.8 \times 10$$
$$= 20.1.$$

The time 10 hours is a long way outside the set of data times; there is no indication that the linear relationship can be extrapolated to such a time, even though there seems to be a good fit, so the prediction is probably unreliable.

(iv) For each pair of data, (x, y), let the predicted value be $\widehat{y} = 2.1 + 1.8x$. Corresponding values of y and $\widehat{y}$ are tabulated below, together with the residuals and their squares.

x	y	$\widehat{y}$	$y - \widehat{y}$	$(y - \widehat{y})^2$
0	2.4	2.1	0.3	0.09
1	4.3	3.9	0.4	0.16
2	5.2	5.7	−0.5	0.25
3	6.8	7.5	−0.7	0.49
4	9.1	9.3	−0.2	0.04
5	11.8	11.1	0.7	0.49
15	39.6	39.6	0.0	1.52

You can see that the sum of the residuals, $\Sigma(y - \widehat{y})$, is zero, and that the sum of the squares of the residuals, $\Sigma(y - \widehat{y})^2$, is 1.52.

Using a graphic calculator

It is fairly easy to set up a graphic calculator to work out the coefficients a and b of the least squares regression line, $y = a + bx$, and to display a scatter diagram. Figure 4.22 shows the output for Example 4.4 obtained by carrying out the following steps.

1 Clear two lists – here list L1 and L2 – and enter the data.
2 Scale both axes.
3 Set up a statistical plot as a scatter diagram, using data from lists L1 and L2.
4 Display the scatter diagram.

5 Display the summary statistics, from which values of a and b may be calculated.

6 Display the coefficients, a and b of the least squares regression line.

7 Enter the equation of the least squares regression line, $y = a + bx$, in the equation editor.

8 Trace the line; enter value(s) of x and read off and plot predicted value(s) of y.

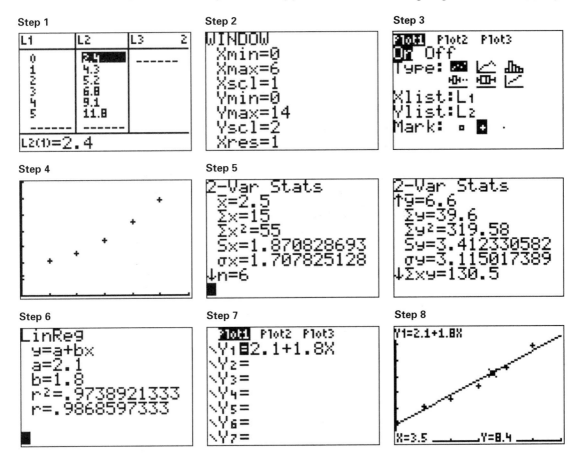

Figure 4.22

 The notation used on this calculator display is not quite the same as that used in the books in this series.

- Sx and Sy both refer to standard deviations (divisor $n - 1$).
- σx and σy both refer to root mean square deviations (divisor n).

Note

The illustrations above are taken from a TI-83 graphic calculator. Similar screen shots are possible from other graphic calculators.

1 For the following bivariate data obtain the equation of the least squares regression line of y on x. Estimate the value of y when $x = 12$.

x	5	10	15	20	25
y	30	28	27	27	21

2 Calculate the equation of the regression line of y on x for the following distribution and use it to estimate the value of y when $x = 42$.

x	25	30	35	40	45	50
y	78	70	65	58	48	42

3 The 1980 and 2000 catalogue prices, in pence, of five British postage stamps are as follows.

1980 price, x	10	20	30	40	50
2000 price, y	100	215	280	360	450

(i) Plot these data on a scatter diagram using graph paper.
(ii) Calculate the equation of the regression line and draw it accurately on your scatter diagram.
(iii) Another stamp was valued at £5 in 1980 and £62 in 2000. Comment.
(iv) Calculate the values of the five residuals and illustrate them on your graph.
(v) Find the sum of the squares of the residuals and relate this to the least squares regression line.

[MEI, *adapted*]

4 The speed of a car, v metres per second, at time t seconds after it starts to accelerate is shown in the table below, for $0 \leqslant t \leqslant 10$.

t	0	1	2	3	4	5	6	7	8	9	10
v	0	3.0	6.8	10.2	12.9	16.4	20.0	21.4	23.0	24.6	26.1

($\Sigma t = 55$, $\Sigma v = 164.4$, $\Sigma t^2 = 385$, $\Sigma v^2 = 3267.98$, $\Sigma tv = 1117.0$.)

The relationship between t and v is initially modelled by using all the data above and calculating a single regression line.

(i) Plot a scatter diagram of the data, with t on the horizontal axis and v on the vertical axis.
(ii) Using all the data given, calculate the equation of the regression line of v on t. Give numerical coefficients in your answers correct to 3 significant figures.
(iii) Calculate the product moment correlation coefficient for the given data.
(iv) Comment on the validity of modelling the data by a single straight line and on the answer obtained in part **(iii)**.

[Cambridge]

5 The results of an experiment to determine how the percentage sand content of soil, y, varies with the depth in centimetres below ground level, x, are given in the following table.

x	0	6	12	18	24	30	36	42	48
y	80.6	63.0	64.3	62.5	57.5	59.2	40.8	46.9	37.6

(i) Illustrate the data by a scatter diagram, drawn on graph paper.

(ii) Calculate the equation of the regression line and plot it on your graph.

(iii) Use your regression equation to predict the values of y for $x = 50$ and $x = 100$. Comment on the validity of your predictions.

(iv) Calculate the residuals and explain why their sum is zero.

[MEI, *adapted*]

6 Observations of a cactus graft were made under controlled environmental conditions. The table gives the observed heights, y cm, of the graft at x weeks after grafting. Also given are the values of $z = \ln y$.

x	1	2	3	4	5	6	8	10
y	2.0	2.4	2.5	5.1	6.7	9.4	18.3	35.1
$z = \ln y$	0.69	0.88	0.92	1.63	1.90	2.24	2.91	3.56

(i) Draw two scatter diagrams, one for y and x, and one for z and x.

(ii) It is desired to estimate the height of the graft seven weeks after grafting. Explain why your scatter diagrams suggest the use of the line of regression of z on x for this purpose, but not the line of regression of y on x.

(iii) Obtain the required estimate given that $\Sigma x = 39$, $\Sigma x^2 = 255$, $\Sigma z = 14.73$, $\Sigma z^2 = 34.5231$, $\Sigma xz = 93.55$.

[MEI]

7 In an experiment on memory, five groups of people (chosen randomly) were given varying lengths of time to memorise the same list of 40 words. Later, they were asked to recall as many words as possible from the list. The table below shows the average number of words recalled, y, and the time given, t seconds.

t	20	40	60	80	100
y	12.1	18.5	22.8	24.6	24.0

(i) Plot the data on a scatter diagram.

(ii) Calculate the equation of the regression line for y on t.

(iii) Use your regression line to predict y when $t = 30$ and $t = 160$. Comment on the usefulness or otherwise of these results.

(iv) Discuss briefly whether the regression line provides a good model or whether there is a better way of modelling the relationship between y and t.

[MEI]

8 A farmer is investigating the relationship between the density at which a crop is planted and the quality. By using more intensive methods he can increase the yield, but he suspects that the percentage of high-quality produce may fall. The farmer collects the following data.

Seed per acre (x) in suitable units	120	130	140	150	160	170
Percentage of high-quality produce (y)	31.3	28.9	25.4	21.3	21.0	10.7

(i) Draw a suitable graph to illustrate the data. Hence discuss how suitable a straight line model would be for the relationship between y and x.

(ii) Calculate the equation of the regression line of y on x and plot it on your graph.

(iii) Obtain from your regression line the predicted values of y at $x = 145$ and $x = 180$. Comment, with reasons, on the likely accuracy of these predictions.

(iv) What role do the residuals play in the derivation of the regression line?

[MEI]

9 A car manufacturer is testing the braking distance for a new model of car. The table shows the braking distance, y metres, for different speeds, x km/hr, when the brakes were applied.

Speed of car, x km/hr	30	50	70	90	110	130
Braking distance, y metres	25	50	85	155	235	350

(i) Plot a scatter diagram on graph paper.

(ii) Calculate the equation of the regression line of y on x. Draw the line on your scatter diagram, together with the residuals.

(iii) Use your regression equation to predict values of y when $x = 100$ and $x = 150$. Comment, with reasons, on the likely accuracy of these predictions.

(iv) Discuss briefly whether the regression line provides a good model or whether there is a better way of modelling the relationship between y and x.

[MEI]

10 The authorities in a school are concerned to ensure that their students enter appropriate mathematics examinations. As part of a research project into this they wish to set up a performance-prediction model. This involves the students taking a standard mid-year test, based on the syllabus and format of the final end-of-year examination.

The school bases its model on the belief that in the final examination students will get the same things right as they did in the mid-year test and in addition a proportion, p, of the things they got wrong.

Consequently a student's final mark, $y\%$, can be predicted on the basis of his or her test mark, $x\%$, by the relationship

$$y = x + p \times (100 - x)$$

Final mark = Test mark + $p \times$ (The marks the student did not get on the test)

Investigate this model, using the following bivariate data. Start by finding the y on x regression line and then rearrange it to estimate p.

x	y	x	y	x	y	x	y
40	55	27	44	60	72	46	70
22	40	32	50	50	70	70	85
10	25	26	49	90	95	33	63
46	68	68	76	30	50	40	60
66	75	54	66	64	80	56	57
8	32	68	70	100	100	45	55
48	69	88	92	44	50	78	85
58	66	48	59	58	62	68	80
50	51	82	90	54	60	78	85
80	85	66	76	24	31	89	91

1 The bivariate sample illustrated in the scatter diagram shows the heights, x cm, and masses, y kg, of a random sample of 20 students.

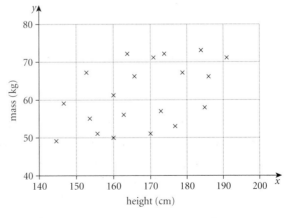

$\Sigma x = 3358$, $\quad \Sigma x^2 = 567\,190$, $\quad \Sigma y = 1225$, $\quad \Sigma y^2 = 76\,357$, $\quad \Sigma xy = 206\,680$.

(i) Calculate the product moment correlation coefficient.

(ii) Carry out a hypothesis test, at the 5% level of significance, to determine whether or not there is evidence that the height of a student is positively correlated with his or her mass. What feature of the scatter diagram suggests that this test is appropriate?

(iii) A statistics student suggests that a positive correlation between height and mass implies that 'the taller a student is the heavier he or she will be'. Comment on this statement with reference to your conclusions in part (ii).

[MEI]

2 A population analyst wishes to test how death rates and birth rates are correlated in European countries.

(i) State appropriate null and alternative hypotheses for the test. Justify the alternative hypothesis you have given.

A random sample of 10 countries from Europe was taken and their death rates (x) and birth rates (y), each per 1000 population for 1997, were noted.

x	9	9	7	12	11	10	7	13	8	7
y	14	9	13	13	10	11	16	9	16	12

(ii) Represent the data graphically.
(iii) Calculate the product moment correlation coefficient.
(iv) Carry out the hypothesis test at the 5% level of significance. State clearly the conclusion reached.

In fact, the value of the product moment correlation coefficient for *all* the countries in Europe in 1997 was -0.555.

(v) What does this tell you about the relationship between death rates and birth rates in European countries?
(vi) State, giving a reason, whether your conclusion in part (iv) is still valid.

[MEI]

3 A student tests whether the amount of daily sunshine and rainfall in the UK are negatively correlated. He uses the following data.

$$n = 25, \qquad \Sigma x = 140.6, \qquad \Sigma y = 77.7,$$
$$\Sigma x^2 = 853.76, \qquad \Sigma y^2 = 492.53, \qquad \Sigma xy = 381.15$$

where x hours is the amount of daily sunshine and y mm is the daily rainfall.

(i) Calculate the product moment correlation coefficient, r.
(ii) Carry out the test at the 2.5% level of significance. State the hypotheses and conclusion carefully.

It is subsequently discovered that the student's data were taken from a newspaper, and that they all relate to UK holiday resorts on the Spring bank holiday.

(iii) Identify two distinct ways in which these data may be thought unsatisfactory.

For the hypothesis test to be valid, daily amounts of sunshine and rainfall must have a particular underlying distribution.

(iv) State what this distribution is and discuss briefly whether or not it is reasonable in this case.

[MEI]

4 A medical statistician wishes to carry out a hypothesis test to see if there is any correlation between the head circumference and body length of newly born babies.

(i) State appropriate null and alternative hypotheses for the test.

A random sample of 20 newly born babies have their head circumference, x cm, and body length, y cm, measured. This bivariate sample is illustrated in the scatter diagram.

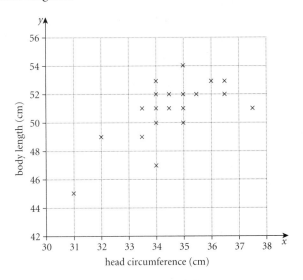

Summary statistics for this data set are as follows.

$$n = 20, \qquad \Sigma x = 691, \qquad \Sigma y = 1018,$$
$$\Sigma x^2 = 23\,917, \qquad \Sigma y^2 = 51\,904, \qquad \Sigma xy = 35\,212.5$$

(ii) Calculate the product moment correlation coefficient for the data. Carry out the hypothesis test at the 1% significance level, stating the conclusion clearly. What assumption is necessary for the test to be valid?

Originally, the point $x = 34$, $y = 51$ had been recorded incorrectly as $x = 51$, $y = 34$.

(iii) Calculate the values of the summary statistics if this error had gone undetected.

Using the uncorrected summary statistics, the value of the product moment correlation coefficient is −0.681 (correct to 3 significant figures).

(iv) How is it that this one error produces such a large change in the value of the correlation coefficient and also changes its sign?

[MEI]

5 Two judges give marks for artistic impression (out of a maximum of 6.0) to ten ice skaters.

Skater	A	B	C	D	E	F	G	H	I	J
Judge 1	5.3	4.9	5.6	5.2	5.7	4.8	5.2	4.6	5.1	4.9
Judge 2	5.4	5.0	5.8	5.6	5.2	4.5	4.7	4.8	5.3	4.9

(i) Calculate the value of Spearman's rank correlation coefficient for the marks of the two judges.

(ii) Use your answer to part **(i)** to test, at the 5% level of significance, whether it appears that there is some overall agreement between the judges. State your hypotheses and your conclusions carefully.

(iii) For these marks the product moment correlation coefficient is 0.6705. Use this to test, at the 5% level, whether there is any positive correlation between the assessments of the two judges.

(iv) Comment on which is the more appropriate test to use in this situation.

[MEI]

6 Bird abundance may be assessed in several ways. In one long-term study in a nature reserve, two independent surveys (A and B) are carried out. The data show the number of wren territories recorded (survey A) and the numbers of adult wrens trapped in a fine mesh net (survey B) over a number of years.

Survey A	16	19	27	50	60	70	79	79	84	85	97
Survey B	11	12	15	18	22	35	35	71	46	53	52

(i) Plot a scatter diagram to compare results for the two surveys.

(ii) Calculate Spearman's coefficient of rank correlation.

(iii) Perform a significance test, at the 5% level, to determine whether there is any association between the results of the two surveys. Explain what your conclusion means in practical terms.

(iv) Would it be more appropriate, less appropriate or equally appropriate to use the product moment correlation coefficient to analyse these data? Explain briefly why.

[MEI]

7 A random sample of ten students who have recently completed their A level studies was taken. Each student was given a points score, based on grades achieved, at both GCSE (x) and A level (y). The distribution of scores is shown below.

x	32	35	36	38	38	40	40	42	43	49
y	6	22	15	9	20	13	11	18	12	30

(i) Represent the data graphically.

(ii) Calculate Spearman's coefficient of rank correlation.

An educational researcher wishes to test whether there is a positive association between students' points scores at GCSE and A level.

(iii) State appropriate null and alternative hypotheses for the test.

(iv) Carry out the hypothesis test at the 5% level of significance. State clearly the conclusion reached.

The product moment correlation coefficient for the data above is 0.5807 (to 4 s.f.).

(v) What conclusion would you reach by conducting a hypothesis test using this value, at the same significance level? Give a reason for your answer.

(vi) Comment on the conclusions reached in parts **(iv)** and **(v)**.

[MEI]

8 A football reporter claims that there is a positive association between the position of a team in its division and the attendance at its next home game. On a Saturday during a season he records the position and attendance for the eleven home teams in Division One, as given in the following table.

Team	Position	Attendance
Barnsley	9th	14 831
Birmingham	4th	17 191
Bolton	3rd	15 585
Burnley	7th	16 107
Grimsby	23rd	4 911
Portsmouth	17th	13 376
Preston	6th	14 511
Sheffield United	8th	12 921
Watford	2nd	17 488
West Bromwich	5th	16 511
Wimbledon	11th	9 030

(i) Rank the positions and the attendances. Carry out an appropriate hypothesis test at the 1% level to test the reporter's claim. State your hypotheses and conclusions clearly, justifying the form of the alternative hypothesis.

(ii) State an assumption about the sample data for the test to be valid. Explain whether or not you think it is appropriate in this case.

(iii) The reporter concludes that 'to increase the attendance at matches, all a team has got to do is climb to a higher position in the division'. Comment critically on the reporter's conclusion.

[MEI]

9 The best times for a 400-metre race in 10 'Olympic' years are as follows.

Years after 1900 (x)	60	64	68	72	76	80	84	88	92	96
Time (y seconds)	55.5	54.2	54.3	52.9	52.3	52.6	50.7	51.0	49.6	48.9

(i) Plot the data on a scatter diagram.

(ii) Calculate the equation of the regression line of y on x.

(iii) Identify an important point through which a regression line must pass, marking this point on your diagram. Draw the regression line on the scatter diagram and indicate the residuals.

(iv) Use your regression equation to predict the best times for the race in the years 2000 and 2020. Comment on the likely accuracy of these predictions.

(v) Explain what part the residuals play in obtaining the equation of a regression line.

[MEI]

10 An experiment was conducted to determine the mass, y g, of a chemical that would dissolve in 100 ml of water at $x\,°C$. The results of the experiment were as follows.

Temperature ($x\,°C$)	10	20	30	40	50
Mass (y g)	61	64	70	73	75

(i) Represent the data on graph paper.

(ii) Calculate the equation of the regression line of y on x. Draw this line on your graph.

(iii) Calculate an estimate of the mass of the chemical that would dissolve in the water at $35\,°C$.

Suggest a range of temperatures for which such estimates are reliable. Give a reason for your answer.

(iv) Calculate the residuals for each of the temperatures. Illustrate them on your graph.

(v) The regression line is often referred to as 'the least squares regression line'. Explain what this means in relation to the residuals.

[MEI]

11 A car manufacturer is introducing a new model. The car is tested for fuel economy three times at each of four different speeds. The values of the fuel economy, y miles per gallon, at each of the speeds, x miles per hour, are displayed in the following table.

x	40	40	40	50	50	50	60	60	60	70	70	70
y	52.7	53.8	54.5	48.1	49.7	51.3	43.3	41.1	48.0	37.5	42.0	44.7

$n = 12$, $\Sigma x = 660$, $\Sigma y = 566.7$, $\Sigma x^2 = 37\,800$, $\Sigma xy = 30\,533$

(i) Represent the data by a scatter diagram, drawn on graph paper.

(ii) Calculate the equation of the regression line of y on x and plot it on your scatter diagram.

(iii) Hence predict the fuel economy of the car at speeds of

    (a) 45 mph

    (b) 65 mph.

(iv) Use your scatter diagram to compare the reliability of your predictions in part **(iii)**.

What do your comments suggest about the validity of a least squares regression line for this data set?

[MEI]

12 A science student took the temperature of a cup of coffee for ten one-minute intervals with the following results.

Time (x minutes)	0	1	2	3	4	5	6	7	8	9	10
Temperature ($y°$C)	96	84	73	64	55	49	44	40	36	33	31

$n = 11$, $\Sigma x = 55$, $\Sigma y = 605$, $\Sigma x^2 = 385$, $\Sigma xy = 2326$

(i) The science student calculates the equation of the least squares regression line of y on x and uses it to predict the temperatures after 4.3 minutes and after 15 minutes.

Obtain the regression line and the predictions. Show that *both* of these predictions are unsatisfactory.

(ii) Plot a scatter diagram on graph paper to illustrate the data. Draw the regression line and the residuals on your diagram. By considering the pattern of the residuals, discuss whether there is a better way of modelling the relationship between temperature and time.

[MEI]

1   A scatter diagram is a graph to illustrate bivariate data.

2   Notation for n pairs of observations (x, y):

$$S_{xx} = \Sigma(x - \overline{x})^2 \equiv \Sigma x^2 - n\overline{x}^2$$
$$S_{yy} = \Sigma(y - \overline{y})^2 \equiv \Sigma y^2 - n\overline{y}^2$$
$$S_{xy} = \Sigma(x - \overline{x})(y - \overline{y}) \equiv \Sigma xy - n\overline{x}\,\overline{y}$$

Correlation

3   Pearson's product moment correlation coefficient,

$$r = \frac{S_{xy}}{\sqrt{S_{xx}S_{yy}}} = \frac{\Sigma(x_i - \overline{x})(y_i - \overline{y})}{\sqrt{\Sigma(x_i - \overline{x})^2\Sigma(y_i - \overline{y})^2}} \equiv \frac{\Sigma x_i y_i - n\overline{x}\,\overline{y}}{\sqrt{(\Sigma x_i^2 - n\overline{x}^2)(\Sigma y_i^2 - n\overline{y}^2)}}.$$

4   Spearman's coefficient of rank correlation,

$$r_s = 1 - \frac{6\Sigma d_i^2}{n(n^2 - 1)}.$$

5   Hypothesis testing:

$$H_0 : \rho = 0$$
$$H_1 : \rho > 0 \text{ or } \rho < 0 \text{ (one-tail test) or } \rho \neq 0 \text{ (two-tail test)}$$

Test the sample value, r, against the critical value, which depends on the number of pairs in the bivariate sample, n, and the significance level.

Regression

6   The equation of the y on x regression line $y = a + bx$ is calculated using $y - \overline{y} = b(x - \overline{x})$, where

$$b = \frac{S_{xy}}{S_{xx}} = \frac{\Sigma(x - \overline{x})(y - \overline{y})}{\Sigma(x - \overline{x})^2} \equiv \frac{\Sigma xy - n\overline{x}\,\overline{y}}{\Sigma x^2 - n\overline{x}^2}$$

$$\Rightarrow \quad a = \overline{y} - b\overline{x}.$$

- For any data pair (x, y) the predicted value of y is
  $\widehat{y} = a + bx \Rightarrow$ residual $\varepsilon = y - \widehat{y}$.
- Sum of residuals $= \Sigma\varepsilon = 0$
- The least squares regression line minimises the sum of the squares of the residuals, $\Sigma\varepsilon^2$.

Appendices

1. Mean and variance of the Poisson distribution

Mean

$$E(X) = \sum_i x_i P(X = x_i) = \sum_{r=0}^{\infty} r P(X = r)$$

$$= 0 + 1 \times P(X = 1) + 2 \times P(X = 2) + 3 \times P(X = 3) + \ldots$$

$$= \frac{1 \times \lambda e^{-\lambda}}{1!} + \frac{2 \times \lambda^2 e^{-\lambda}}{2!} + \frac{3 \times \lambda^3 e^{-\lambda}}{3!} + \ldots$$

$$= \lambda e^{-\lambda} \left(1 + \lambda + \frac{\lambda^2}{2!} + \frac{\lambda^3}{3!} + \ldots \right)$$

The series in the brackets $= e^{\lambda}$, therefore

$$E(X) = \lambda e^{-\lambda} e^{\lambda}$$

$$= \lambda$$

Variance

$$Var(X) = E(X^2) - [E(X)]^2$$

$$E(X^2) = \sum_{r=0}^{\infty} r^2 P(X = r)$$

Putting
$$r^2 = r(r - 1) + r$$

gives
$$E(X^2) = \sum_{r=0}^{\infty} \{r(r - 1) + r\} P(X = r)$$

$$= \sum_{r=0}^{\infty} r(r - 1) P(X = r) + \sum_{r=0}^{\infty} r P(X = r)$$

Now $\displaystyle\sum_{r=0}^{\infty} r P(X = r) = \lambda$, therefore

$$E(X^2) = \sum_{r=0}^{\infty} r(r - 1) P(X = r) + \lambda$$

Now the first term, $\displaystyle\sum_{r=0}^{\infty} r(r - 1) P(X = r)$

$$= 0 + 0 + 2 \times 1 \times P(X = 2) + 3 \times 2 \times P(X = 3)$$

$$+ 4 \times 3 \times P(X = 4) + \ldots$$

$$= \frac{2 \times 1 \times \lambda^2 e^{-\lambda}}{2!} + \frac{3 \times 2 \times \lambda^3 e^{-\lambda}}{3!}$$

$$+ \frac{4 \times 3 \times \lambda^4 e^{-\lambda}}{4!} + \ldots$$

Cancelling
$$= \lambda^2 e^{-\lambda} + \lambda^3 e^{-\lambda} + \frac{\lambda^4 e^{-\lambda}}{2!} + \frac{\lambda^5 e^{-\lambda}}{3!} + \dots$$

$$= \lambda^2 e^{-\lambda}\left(1 + \lambda + \frac{\lambda^2}{2!} + \frac{\lambda^3}{3!} + \dots\right)$$

Once again the term in brackets $= e^{\lambda}$

$$= \lambda^2 e^{-\lambda} e^{\lambda}$$

$$= \lambda^2$$

This now gives:

$$\mathrm{E}(X^2) = \lambda^2 + \lambda$$

So that:

$$\mathrm{Var}(X) = \lambda^2 + \lambda - \lambda^2$$

$$= \lambda$$

Thus showing that for the Poisson distribution the mean and variance are both λ.

2. The sum of two independent Poisson distributions

Suppose that $X \sim \text{Poisson}\ (\lambda)$ and $Y \sim \text{Poisson}\ (\mu)$ and that X and Y are independent, and that T is the random variable given by

$$T = X + Y.$$

$$P(T = t) = P(X = t) \times P(Y = 0) + P(X = t - 1) \times P(Y = 1)$$
$$+ P(X = t - 2) \times P(Y = 2) + \dots + P(X = 0) \times P(Y = t)$$

X and Y must be independent so that the probabilities can be multiplied.

$$= \frac{\lambda^t e^{-\lambda} e^{-\mu}}{t!} + \frac{\lambda^{t-1} e^{-\lambda} \mu e^{-\mu}}{(t-1)!1!} + \frac{\lambda^{t-2} e^{-\lambda} \mu^2 e^{-\mu}}{(t-2)!2!} + \dots + \frac{e^{-\lambda} \mu^t e^{-\mu}}{t!}$$

$$= e^{-(\lambda+\mu)}\left\{\frac{\lambda^t}{t!} + \frac{\lambda^{t-1}\mu}{(t-1)!1!} + \frac{\lambda^{t-2}\mu^2}{(t-1)!2!} + \dots + \frac{\mu^t}{t!}\right\}$$

$$= \frac{e^{-(\lambda+\mu)}}{t!}\left\{\lambda^t + \frac{t!\lambda^{t-1}\mu}{(t-1)!1!} + \frac{t!\lambda^{t-2}\mu^2}{(t-2)!2!} + \dots + \mu^t\right\}$$

Now the term in brackets is just the binomial expansion of $(\lambda + \mu)^t$ so

$$P(T = t) = \frac{e^{-(\lambda+\mu)}(\lambda + \mu)^t}{t!}$$

which is the Poisson probability with parameter $\lambda + \mu$.

So the sum of the two independent Poisson distributions with parameters λ and μ is itself a Poisson distribution with parameter $\lambda + \mu$.

Similarly, the sum of n independent Poisson distributions with parameters $\lambda_1, \lambda_2, \dots, \lambda_n$ is a Poisson distribution with parameter $(\lambda_1 + \lambda_2 + \dots + \lambda_n)$.

3. The equivalence of Spearman's rank correlation coefficient and Pearson's product moment correlation coefficient

Let the ranks assigned to n items by two judges be $x_1, x_2, \ldots, x_n$ and $y_1, y_2, \ldots, y_n$.

$$
\begin{array}{ccccccc}
x_1 & x_2 & \cdots & x_i & \cdots & x_n \\
y_1 & y_2 & \cdots & y_i & \cdots & y_n \\
\end{array}
$$

$$|d_i| = |x_1 - y_1| \quad |x_2 - y_2| \quad \cdots \quad |x_i - y_i| \quad \cdots \quad |x_n - y_n|$$

$$\sum_{i=1}^{n} d_i^2 = \sum_{i=1}^{n} (x_i - y_i)^2 = \sum_i x_i^2 + \sum_i y_i^2 - 2 \sum_i x_i y_i$$

Since the values of $x_1, \ldots, x_n$ and $y_1, \ldots, y_n$ are both $1, 2, 3, \ldots, n$ in some order

$$\sum_{i=1}^{n} x_i = \sum_{i=1}^{n} y_i = \frac{n(n+1)}{2}$$

$$\bar{x} = \bar{y} = \frac{n+1}{2}$$

$$\sum_{i=1}^{n} x_i^2 = \sum_{i=1}^{n} y_i^2 = \frac{n(n+1)(2n+1)}{6}$$

$$S_{xx} \sum_{i=1}^{n} x_i^2 - n\bar{x}^2 = \frac{n(n+1)(2n+1)}{6} - n\left(\frac{n+1}{2}\right)^2$$

$$= \frac{n(n+1)(n-1)}{12} = \frac{n(n^2-1)}{12} = \sum_{i=1}^{n} y_i^2 - n\bar{y}^2 = S_{yy}$$

$$r_s = 1 - \frac{6\Sigma d_i^2}{n(n^2-1)}$$

$$= 1 - \frac{6[\Sigma x_i^2 + \Sigma y_i^2 - 2\Sigma x_i y_i]}{n(n^2-1)}$$

$$= \frac{1}{n(n^2-1)} \times \left\{ n(n^2-1) \right.$$
$$\left. - 6\left[\frac{n(n+1)(2n+1)}{6} + \frac{n(n+1)(2n+1)}{6} - 2\Sigma x_i y_i \right] \right\}$$

$$= \frac{12\Sigma x_i y_i - 3n(n+1)^2}{n(n^2-1)}$$

$$= \frac{12\left[\Sigma x_i y_i - n\left(\frac{n+1}{2}\right)^2 \right]}{n(n^2-1)}$$

$$= \frac{\Sigma x_i y_i - n\bar{x}\bar{y}}{\sqrt{\left(\frac{n(n^2-1)}{12}\right)\left(\frac{n(n^2-1)}{12}\right)}} = \frac{S_{xy}}{\sqrt{S_{xx}S_{yy}}}$$

$$= r \qquad \text{as required}$$

4. The least squares regression line

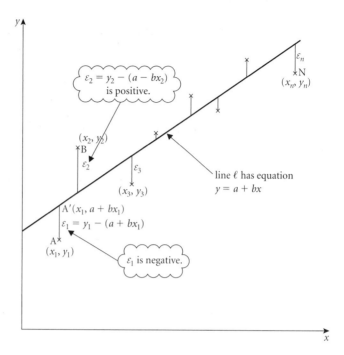

Figure A4.1

The least squares regression line for the set of bivariate data $(x_1, y_1), (x_2, y_2), \ldots,$ (x_n, y_n) is of the form $y = a + bx$ with the values of a and b giving the minimum sum of the squares of the residuals, $\varepsilon_1, \varepsilon_2, \ldots, \varepsilon_n$.

Since $\varepsilon_r = y_r - a + bx_r$, the values of a and b which minimise

$$T = \sum_{r=1}^{n} (y_r - a + bx_r)^2 \text{ must be found.}$$

This is the same as $T = \sum_{r=1}^{n} (a + bx_r - y_r)^2$. The proof which follows uses this form (which, with a at the front, is perhaps slightly easier to follow).

$$T = \sum_{r=1}^{n} (a + bx_r - y_r)^2$$

$$= \sum_{r=1}^{n} [a + (bx_r - y_r)]^2$$

$$= \sum_{r=1}^{n} [a^2 + 2a(bx_r - y_r) + (bx_r - y_r)^2]$$

$$= na^2 + 2a \sum_{r=1}^{n} (bx_r - y_r) + \sum_{r=1}^{n} (bx_r - y_r)^2$$

$$= n\left[a^2 + \frac{2a}{n} \sum_{r=1}^{n} (bx_r - y_r) + \frac{1}{n} \sum_{r=1}^{n} (bx_r - y_r)^2\right]$$

You can treat the right-hand side of the expression on the previous page as a quadratic in a. Completing the square on it

$$T = n \left\{ a^2 + \frac{2a}{n} \sum_{r=1}^{n} (bx_r - y_r) + \frac{1}{n^2} \left[\sum_{r=1}^{n} (bx_r - y_r) \right]^2 \right.$$

$$\left. + \frac{1}{n} \sum_{r=1}^{n} (bx_r - y_r)^2 - \frac{1}{n^2} \left[\sum_{r=1}^{n} (bx_r - y_r) \right]^2 \right\}$$

$$= n \left[a + \frac{1}{n} \sum_{r=1}^{n} (bx_r - y_r) \right]^2 + \sum_{r=1}^{n} (bx_r - y_r)^2 - \frac{1}{n} \left[\sum_{r=1}^{n} (bx_r - y_r) \right]^2$$

$$= n \left[a - \frac{1}{n} \sum_{r=1}^{n} (y_r - bx_r) \right]^2 + \sum_{r=1}^{n} (bx_r - y_r)^2 - \frac{1}{n} \left[\sum_{r=1}^{n} (bx_r - y_r) \right]^2$$

The last two terms do not involve a and so if we wish to choose a so as to minimise T it seems sensible to let

$$a = \frac{1}{n} \sum_{r=1}^{n} (y_r - bx_r),$$

for then the first term on the right-hand side becomes zero and this term was of course a non-negative one.

This means

$$a = \frac{1}{n} \sum_{r=1}^{n} y_r - \frac{b}{n} \sum_{r=1}^{n} x_r.$$

$$\Rightarrow \qquad a = \bar{y} - b\bar{x} \qquad\qquad\qquad\qquad ①$$

Since the equation of the required regression line is $y = ax + b$, equation ① just means that we wish the regression line to pass through $(\bar{x}, \bar{y})$. This is clearly sensible since $(\bar{x}, \bar{y})$ is the mean point and so approximately the centre of the scatter diagram.

$$T = \sum_{r=1}^{n} (a + bx_r - y_r)^2$$

Substitute now for a from equation ①,

$$T = \sum_{r=1}^{n} (\bar{y} - b\bar{x} + bx_r - y_r)^2$$

By reversing all signs

$$T = \sum_{r=1}^{n} [(y_r - \bar{y}) - b(x_r - \bar{x})]^2$$

$$= \sum_{r=1}^{n} (y_r - \bar{y})^2 - 2b \sum_{r=1}^{n} (x_r - \bar{x})(y_r - \bar{y}) + b^2 \sum_{r=1}^{n} (x_r - \bar{x})^2$$

$$= S_{yy} - 2bS_{xy} + b^2 S_{xx}$$

$$= S_{xx} \left[b^2 - 2b \frac{S_{xy}}{S_{xx}} + \frac{S_{yy}}{S_{xx}} \right]$$

Now you can treat the square bracket as a quadratic in b. Again, complete the square.

$$T = S_{xx} \left[b^2 - 2b \frac{S_{xy}}{S_{xx}} + \left(\frac{S_{xy}}{S_{xx}} \right)^2 + \frac{S_{yy}}{S_{xx}} - \left(\frac{S_{xy}}{S_{xx}} \right)^2 \right]$$

$$= S_{xx} \left[\left(b - \frac{S_{xy}}{S_{xx}} \right)^2 + \frac{S_{yy}}{S_{xx}} - \left(\frac{S_{xy}}{S_{xx}} \right)^2 \right]$$

The last two terms on the right-hand side are constants for the distribution and so to minimise T you set the first term in the square bracket on the right-hand side equal to zero, i.e.

$$b = \frac{S_{xy}}{S_{xx}}$$

The regression line to minimise T is now

$$y = a + bx$$

$$= (\bar{y} - b\bar{x}) + bx$$

$$\Rightarrow \quad y - \bar{y} = b(x - \bar{x})$$

$$\Rightarrow \quad y - \bar{y} = \frac{S_{xy}}{S_{xx}} (x - \bar{x})$$

and this equation is called the least squares regression line of y on x.

Answers

Chapter 1

Exercise 1A (Page 7)

1 (i) 0.266
  (ii) 0.826
2 (i) 0.2942
  (ii) 0.1747
  (iii) 0.2092
3 (i) 0.224
  (ii) 0.185
  (iii) 0.815
4 (i) (a) 0.7916
       (b) 0.1251
       (c) 0.7798
  (ii) 0.343
5 X may be modelled by a Poisson distribution when cars arrive singly and independently and at a known overall average rate.
   0.442
6 0.79
   It is assumed that calls arrive singly and independently and with a known overall average rate of 4.2 calls per night.
7 (i) 0.058
  (ii) 0.099
8 (i) 25
  (ii) 75
  (iii) 112
  (iv) 278
   Assume that mistakes occur randomly, singly, independently and at a constant mean rate.
9 (i) 0.111, 0.244, 0.268, 0.377
  (ii) 3
10 600 m;
    Poisson distribution with parameter 2.5;
    0.082, 0.109;   0.779, 0.207
11 (i) 3
   (ii) 27.5
   (iii) 460
12 (i) 0.165
   (ii) 5
   (iii) 0.027
   (iv) 5
13 (i) The mean is much greater than the variance therefore X does not have a Poisson distribution.
   (ii) Yes because now the values of the mean and variance are similar.
   (iii) 0.012

14 (i) 0.175
   (ii) 0.560
   (iii) 0.1251
   (iv) 0.5421
   (v) 0.0308; 10
15 Some bottles will contain two or more hard particles. This will decrease the percentage of bottles that have to be discarded.
    13.9%
    Assume the hard particles occur singly, independently and randomly.
16 $X \sim$ Poisson(1); 0.014; 0.205
17 (i) 0.738
   (ii) 239, 177, 65, 16, 0, 0
   (iii) 239.0, 176.4, 65.1, 16.0, 3.0, 0.4
   (iv) Yes, there seems to be reasonable agreement between the actual data and the Poisson predictions.
18 Because we assume injuries occur singly, independently and randomly.
    0.5, 0.48; because the mean is approximately equal to the variance.
    31.5, 15.8, 3.9, 0.7, 0.1
19 7.03, 6.84;
    The mean is approximately equal to the variance.
    8.17
20 3.87, 3.53, taking $f_9 = 8$
    Poisson distribution with parameter 3.87 because radioactive atoms decay randomly and independently and at a constant mean rate if the half-life is long compared with the duration of the experiment.
    10.8, 41.9, 81.1, 104.6, 101.2, 78.3, 50.5, 27.9. 13.5, 9.2
    There is quite good agreement between the two sets of figures.
    75.8

❓ (Page 15)

1 It is not necessarily so that a car or lorry passing along the road is a random event. Regular users will change both Poisson parameters which in turn will affect the solution to the problem.
2 No. Traffic tends to travel in a line at the same speed on some roads.
3 It could be that their numbers are negligible or it might be assumed they do not damage the cattle grid.

Exercise 1B (Page 15)

1 (i)   0.102
   (ii) 0.285
   (iii) 0.422
2 (i)   0.175
   (ii) 0.973
   (iii) 0.031; 0.125; 0.249
3 (i)   (a) 0.082
         (b) 0.456
   (ii) 0.309
   (iii) 1 east-bound and 2 west-bound
4 (i)   (a) 0.180
         (b) 0.264
         (c) 0.916
   (ii) 0.296
   (iii) 0.549
5 (i)   0.189
   (ii) 0.308
   (iii) 0.184
6 (i)   0.301
   (ii) 0.080
   (iii) 0.251
7 (i)   (a) 0.007
         (b) 0.034
         (c) 0.084
   (ii) $T \sim$ Poisson (5.0)
8 (i)   (a) 0.134
         (b) 0.848
   (ii) 0.086
   (iii) 0.673
9 (i)   (a) 0.257
         (b) 0.223
         (c) 0.168
   (ii) 0.340
10 (i)   0.531
   (ii) 0.065
   (iii) 0.159

Exercise 1C (Page 23)

1 (i)   0.135 768, 0.140 374, 3.4%
   (ii) 0.140 078, 0.140 374, 0.2%
   (iii) 0.140 346, 0.140 374, 0.02%
2 (i)   0.224
   (ii) 0.392
3 (i)   0.104
   (ii) 0.560
   (iii) 0.762
4 (i)   0.125
   (ii) 0.458
5 (i)   0.3328
   (ii) 0.0016

6 (i)   0.362
   (ii) 0.544
   (iii) 0.214
   (iv) 0.558
7 (i)   0.082
   (ii) 0.891
   (iii) 0.287
8 (i)   0.161
   (ii) 0.554
   (iii) 10
   (iv) 0.016
   (v)   0.119
9 (i)   0.47
   (ii) 0.04
   The binomial model assumes that the probability of dialling a wrong number is the same for whatever phone call is made. This is questionable since one might expect a greater likelihood of an error when dialling long distance or unfamiliar numbers than when dialling local or frequently used numbers. It seems sensible to use the Poisson approximation since n is large and p is small and the corresponding Poisson parameter, 0.75, is simple to use.
10 (i)   (a) The distribution of X is approximately binomial, n is large, p is small and $\lambda = np = 20$.
         (b) 0.86
   (ii) 230
11 (i)   0.323
   (ii) 0.012

Exercise 1D (page 26)

1 (i)   Binomial; Poisson; because n is large and p is small.
   (ii) $P(X = 0) = 0.0074$; probability is small so it is unlikely.
   (iii) 0.0421
   (iv) 0.000 213
2 (i) $X \sim B(150, \frac{1}{80})$; $X \sim$ Poisson (1.875); The Poisson distribution is a suitable approximating distribution because n is large and p is small.
   (ii) 0.559
   (iii) $n \geqslant 367$ (binomial) or $n \geqslant 369$ (Poisson)
3 (i)   0.27
   (ii) 0.3504
   (iii) 0.182 (3 s.f.)
   (iv) $\lambda = 10.5$; $P(X = 10) = 0.1236$; The car hire firm only has three cars and so cannot hire more than three cars on any given day; this is not taken into account in the calculation.
   (v)   Expected daily profit = £32.42

4 (i) $X \sim \mathrm{B}(2040, \frac{1}{6000})$; n is large and p is small; $\lambda = 0.34$

   (ii) 0.242

   (iii) $\lambda = 10.2$, $P(X \geqslant 12) = 1 - 0.6738 = 0.3262$

   (iv) $k = 5$

       $P(X \leqslant 3) < 1\%$ implies the model is not appropriate; either one or more of the parameters is incorrect or the assumption of independence is not valid.

5 (i) Incidents occur at a uniform average rate independently of each other.

   (ii) (a) $\lambda = 2$, $P(X = 2) = 0.2707$

      (b) 0.0183

      (c) $\lambda = 8$, $P(Y > 10) = 1 - 0.8159 = 0.1841$

6 (i) (a) 0.270 (3 s.f.)

      (b) 0.001 44

      (c) 0.491

   (ii) $\lambda = -\ln(0.2) = 1.6094 \approx 1.61$

   (iii) 0.1896

   (iv) 0.369

7 (i) $X \sim \mathrm{B}(108, 0.05)$; It must be assumed that whether or not each person turns up is independent of whether or not any other person turns up.

   (ii) (a) 0.12 (2 s.f.)

      (b) 0.37 (2 s.f.)

      (c) 0.29 (2 s.f.)

   (iii) £85 or £86

8 (i) (a) 0.485 (3 s.f.)

      (b) 0.116 (3 s.f.)

      (c) 0.087 (2 s.f.)

   (ii) The Poisson parameter is unlikely to be the same for each team and there is a lack of independence.

9 (i) $X \sim \mathrm{B}(500, 0.01)$

   (ii) 0.7419

   (iii) 0.049 (to 2 s.f.)

10 (i) Mean = 1.84, variance = 1.75 (3 s.f.)

   (ii) Independence of arrival and random distribution through time or uniform average rate of occurrence or mean and variance approximately equal or n is large and p is small.

   (iii) 26.9 days

   (iv) 0.410 (3 s.f.)

   (v) 0.0424

11 (i) $X \sim \mathrm{B}(n, 0.04)$; to be valid, you must assume independence of lateness of arrival of trains. For a Poisson approximation to be appropriate, n must be large.

   (ii) 0.167 (3 s.f.); 2.1%

   (iii) 0.554

   (iv) Smallest value of $k = 17$; the rail watchdog would tolerate up to 16 late arrivals; if the watchdog found there to be 17 or more late arrivals in a ten-week period, then the probability of this occurring with $p = 0.04$ is so small that a significant deterioration in punctuality could be detected.

12 (i) $X \sim \mathrm{B}(25, 0.05)$; $P(X = 2) = 0.231$

   (ii) $\lambda = 9.2$; n is large and p is small

   (iii) 0.318 (3 s.f.)

   (iv) 15

   (v) $P(X \geqslant 20) = 0.0014$, which is unlikely suggesting that there is a lack of independence or that less than 95% of the adults who have a flu jab in October do not catch flu.

13 (i) Because n is large and p is small or because there is a uniform rate of occurrence or the occurrences are independent.

   (ii) 2.7, 2.67; the mean and variance are approximately equal, which further supports the Poisson model.

   (iii)

Number of light bulbs, x	Expected frequencies
0	6.72
1	18.15
2	24.50
3	22.05
4	14.88
5	8.04
6	3.62
7+	2.06

The relatively large discrepancies between the expected and observed frequencies cast doubt on the Poisson model.

   (iv) Poisson (675); tables do not go up to $\lambda = 675$ and calculations are likely to require a lot of terms to be evaluated; a suitable approximating distribution is the Normal distribution, N(675, 675).

Chapter 2

Exercise 2A (Page 44)

1 (i) 0.8413

   (ii) 0.0228

   (iii) 0.1359

2 (i) 0.0668

   (ii) 0.6915

   (iii) 0.2417

3 (i) 0.0668

(ii) 0.1587

(iii) 0.7745

4 (i) 0.0038

(ii) 0.5

(iii) 0.495

5 (i) 31, 1.97

(ii) 2.1, 13.4, 34.5, 34.5, 13.4, 2.1

(iii) More data would need to be taken to say reliably that the weights are Normally distributed.

6 (i) 5.48%

(ii) (a) 25 425 km

(b) 1843 km

7 (i) 78.65%

(ii) 5.254, 0.054

8 (i) 20.3%

(ii) 81.0 g

9 (i) 0.0765

(ii) 0.2216

(iii) 0.4315

10 (i) 0.077

(ii) 0.847

(iii) 0.674

(iv) 1.313 m

11 (i) 0.0900

(ii) 0.5392

(iii) 0.3467

(iv) 8.28 and 30 s

12 0.0401

(i) 0.4593

(ii) 0.003

13 (i) (a) 0.675

(b) 0.325

(ii) 0.481

(iii) 31 days

14 20.05, 0.0248, 0.7794, 22.6%

15 0.0312

(i) 0.927

(ii) 0.08

16 11.09%, 0.0123, 0.0243

❓ (Page 52)

One possibility is that some people, knowing their votes should be secret, resented being asked who they had supported and so deliberately gave wrong answers. Another is that the exit poll was taken at a time of day when those voting were unrepresentative of the electorate as a whole.

Exercise 2B (Page 54)

1 99.4% of the population have IQs less than 2.5 standard deviations above the mean.

0.165

2 (i) 106

(ii) 75 and 125

(iii) 39.5

3 (i) 0.282

(ii) 0.526

(iii) (a) 25

(b) 4.33

(iv) 0.102

4 0.246, 0.0796, 0.0179

The Normal distribution is used for continuous data; the binomial distribution is used for discrete data. If a Normal approximation to the binomial distribution is used then a continuity correction must be made. Without this the result would not be accurate.

5 n must be large and p must not be too close to 0 or 1. These conditions ensure that the distribution is reasonably symmetrical so that its probability profile resembles a Normal distribution.

(i) 0.1853

(ii) 0.1838

(iii) 0.81%

6 (i) (a) 0.315

(b) 0.307; assuming the answer to part **(i) (a)** is correct, there is a 7.6% error; worse

(ii) 0.5245

7 $\frac{1}{3}$; 6.667; 4.444; 13

8 (i) 0.590

(ii) 0.081

It is assumed that the defective syringes are mixed randomly with the functional ones. Also, as the total number of syringes in the box is very large, removing one syringe leaves the probability distribution of defective and functional syringes unchanged. It may be convenient to use the Normal approximation as this simplifies the probability calculation. So long as a continuity correction is made the result ought to be very close to the binomial model result.

$P(X \geqslant 15) = 0.067$

9 $^{2000}C_N \left(\dfrac{1}{30}\right)^N \left(\dfrac{29}{30}\right)^{2000-N}$

86; more (96)

10 (i) X has a binomial distribution with $p = 0.8$ i.e. $X \sim B(n, 0.8)$; 0.9389

(ii) $X \sim N(80, 16)$; 0.0845

(iii) 71

11 0.180; 60, 7.75, 0.9124

12 Mean $= \sum_{r=0}^{\infty} r\mathrm{P}(X = r) = \lambda$, called the Poisson parameter.

Variance $= \mathrm{E}(X^2) - \lambda^2 = \lambda$

The Poisson parameter should be greater than 10 so that the probability profile is approximately bell-shaped.

   (i) 0.0222

   (ii) 0.9778

13 (i) 2.5; assume that service calls occur singly, independently and randomly.

   (ii) 0.918, 0.358

   (iii) 0.158

14 (i) 0.4928

   (ii) 0.0733

   (iii) 0.6865

15 (i) 0.7620

   (ii) 0.0329

   (iii) 0.3536

16 (i) 0.188

   (ii) 0.9906

   (iii) (a) 0.9629

      (b) 1.0000

      Four lots of 50 is only one of many ways to make 200, so you would expect the probability in part **(b)** to be higher than that in part **(a)**.

17 (i) (a) 0.6144

      (b) 0.8342

      (c) 0.9995

   (ii) You must assume that the same number of emails will be received, on average, in the future.

   (iii) For longer time periods, there are more and more different ways in which the total can be reached, so the probability increases.

18 (i) (a) Poisson (10)

      (b) N(100, 100)

   (ii) 0.0363; 0.0352; The approximation is good, as the error is only 3%.

   (iii) 0.4176

   (iv) $a = 74.2$, $b = 125.8$

Exercise 2C (Page 59)

1 (i)

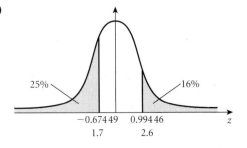

   (ii) 2.0637, 0.5393; because the values have been calculated from a sample, not the whole population.

   (iii) 2735

2 (i) $\mathrm{P}(X < 1) = 0.51\%$

   (ii) (a) 0.8867

      (b) 0.9936

   (iii) 18

   (iv) $Y \sim \mathrm{N}(18, 17.91)$; 0.2774

3 (i) 0.8944

   (ii) 968.4

   (iii) $\mathrm{P} = 0.5119$

   (iv) 909.04

4 (i) 0.0353

   (ii) 49.32, 6.906

   (iii) $Y \sim \mathrm{N}(49.32, 6.906^2)$, 0.0527

   (iv) 38

   (v) 32 returns seems suspiciously low, check to see if there are any omissions.

5 (i)

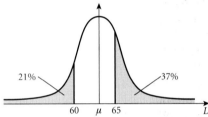

   (ii) $65 = \mu + 0.3319\sigma$; $60 = \mu - 0.8064\sigma$, $\mu = 63.542$, $\sigma = 4.393$

   (iii) $\mathrm{P}(L > 70) = 7.08\%$; this is consistent with the distribution found in part **(ii)**.

   (iv) $\mathrm{P}(L < 55) = 2.59\%$; this is inconsistent with the distribution found in part **(ii)**.

6 (i) (a) 0.0563

      (b) 0.2241

   (ii) $X \sim \mathrm{N}(25, \frac{75}{4})$, 0.092

   (iii) $\mathrm{P}(X \geqslant 40) = 0.0004$

   (iv) Bella's expected score is 43.75, which is greater than 40. She is therefore likely to pass because of the symmetry of the distribution.

7 (i) There is a uniform rate of occurrence over time. Mean $= 2040$, standard deviation $= 45.17$

   (ii) 0.1848

   (iii) 1951, 2129

   (iv) 747 000

8 (i)

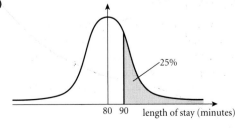

Mean = 80, standard deviation = 14.83

(ii) 0.0038

(iii) According to the model, large numbers of children arriving at 4 pm stay beyond closing time.

(iv) Taking the longest length of stay to be 125 minutes, the latest time of arrival for which the model is reasonable is about 2.55 pm.

9 (i) **(a)** 0.2226

    (b) 0.6201

    (c) 0.6163

(ii) 0.1380

(iii) $Y \sim N(128, 128)$, 0.9941

(iv) It suggests the mean is too high.

10 (i)

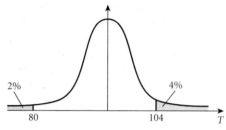

(ii) $80 = \mu - 2.054\sigma$; $104 = \mu + 1.751\sigma$,
$\mu = 92.96$, $\sigma = 6.307$

(iii) 17%

(iv) 81.24

11 (i) 0.29

(ii) 4340

(iii) Because the probability of scoring between 0 and 10 is about 0.99.

(iv) 0.0258

(v) 113 or more

12 (i)

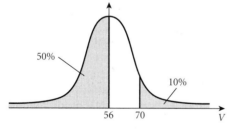

(ii) 56, 10.92; The values are estimates because they are based on a sample, not the population.

(iii) 70.85%

(iv) 27.9 mph to 84.1 mph

(v) The speeds of the cars may not be independent and the distribution of speeds may not be symmetrical.

13 (i)

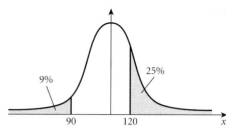

(ii) $90 = -1.341\sigma + \mu$, $120 = 0.6745\sigma + \mu$,
$\sigma = 14.88$, $\mu = 109.96$

(iii) 0.9363

(iv) 107 g

14 (i) 0.0548

(ii) $15.98 \approx 16$

(iii) 0.899 (3 d.p.)

(iv) 15.45 (2 d.p.)

(v) Reduce the standard deviation

15 (i) $X \sim B(n, 0.35)$

(ii) 0.8818

(iii) 0.751

(iv) $a \approx 311$, $b \approx 389$

(v) The probability of 400 voters out of 1000 saying they would vote Liberal Democrat is so small that it suggests that this proportion has increased.

16 (i) 0.465 (3 s.f.)

(ii) 0857 or 0858

(iii) **(a)** 0.0228

    (b) 0.995 (3 s.f.)

(iv) 0830

17 (i) The statistics are symmetrical about the median.

(ii)

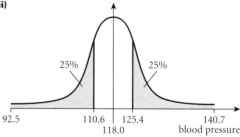

(iii) $\mu = 118$

(iv) 0.34 (2 s.f.)

(v) 18

18 (i) **(a)** 0.025 (2 s.f.)

    (b) 0.242 (3 s.f.)

(ii) 130

(iii) 0.161 (3 s.f.)

(iv) 0.0334

19 (i)

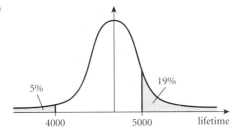

(ii) $\mu = 4650$

(iii) 0.44 (2 s.f.)

(iv) 3700 hours

(v) 0.76 (2 s.f.)

20 (i)

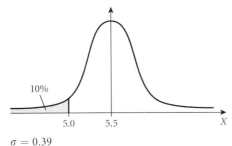

$\sigma = 0.39$

(ii) 0.4649

(iii) 0.243 (3 s.f.)

(iv) 0.962 (3 s.f.)

Chapter 3

❓ (Page 71)

In this case $\mu = 30$, $\sigma = 5$ and $n = 4$ so

$$\frac{\sigma^2}{n} = \frac{25}{4} = 6.25 = 2.5^2.$$

Exercise 3A (Page 76)

1 (i) $z = 1.53$, not significant

(ii) $z = -2.37$, significant

(iii) $z = 1.57$, not significant

(iv) $z = 2.25$, significant

(v) $z = -2.17$, significant

2 (i) 0.3085

(ii) 0.016

(iii) 0.0062

(iv) $H_0: \mu = 4.00$ g, $H_1: \mu > 4.00$ g

$z = 3$, significant

3 (i) $H_0: \mu = 72.7$ g, $H_1: \mu \neq 72.7$ g; Two-tail test.

(ii) $z = 1.84$, not significant

(iii) No, significant

4 (i) $H_0: \mu = 23.9°$, $H_1: \mu > 23.9°$

(ii) $z = 1.29$, significant

(iii) 4.42; This is much greater than 2.3 so the ecologist should be asking whether the temperature has become more variable.

5 (i) You must assume it has a Normal distribution.

(ii) $H_0: \mu = 470$ days, $H_1: \mu > 470$ days

(iii) $z = 3.02$, significant

(iv) More time to produce offspring.

6 (i) You must assume that the speeds are Normally distributed.

(ii) $H_0: \mu = 80$ mph, $H_1: \mu \neq 80$ mph

$z = 2.28$, significant

(iii) Yes: $z = 1.33$, not significant

7 (i) You must assume that the visibilities are Normally distributed.

(ii) $H_0: \mu = 14$ sea miles, $H_1: \mu < 14$ sea miles

(iii) $z = -2.284$, significant

(iv) Choosing 36 consecutive days to collect data is not a good idea because weather patterns will ensure that the data are not independent. A better sampling procedure would be to choose every tenth day. In this way the effects of weather patterns over the year would be eliminated.

8 $H_1: \mu \neq 1$ kg; $z = -1.79$, not significant
$H_1: \mu < 1$ kg; $z = -1.79$, significant.

9 $H_0: \mu = 50$ kg, $H_1: \mu < 50$ kg;
Yes: $z = -1.875$, significant

10 (i) $N(190, 5.\dot{3})$

(ii) The skulls in group B have greater mean lengths and so a one-tail test is required.

(iii) 193.8

(iv) Significant

11 (i) 998.6, 7.000

(ii) $H_0: \mu = 1000$, $H_1: \mu < 1000$

(iii) $z = -1.59$, not significant

12 $H_0: \mu = 0$, $H_1: \mu \neq 0$; $z = 0.98$, not significant

13 (i) 16.2, 5.196

(ii) $H_0: \mu = 15$, $H_1: \mu > 15$

(iii) $z = 2$, not significant

14 (i) 1.977, 0.131

(ii) $H_0: \mu = 2$, $H_1: \mu < 2$

(iii) $z = -1.68$, not significant

15 (i) 104.7, 3.000

(ii) $H_0: \mu = 105$, $H_1: \mu \neq 105$

(iii) $z = -0.89$, not significant

Exercise 3B (Page 92)

1 $X^2 = 2.886$

$v = 1$

Accept H_0 at 5% level or below: independent

2 $X^2 = 35.87$

$v = 12$

Reject H_0 at 5% level or above: association

3 $X^2 = 0.955$

$v = 1$

Accept H_0 at 10% level or below: no association

4 $X^2 = 7.137$

$v = 4$

Accept H_0 at 10% level or below: independent

5 $X^2 = 10.38$

$v = 1$

Reject H_0 at 1% level (c.v. $= 6.635$): related

6 $X^2 = 13.27$

$v = 6$

Reject H_0 at 2.5% level or above: not independent

7 $X^2 = 11.354$

$v = 4$

Reject H_0 at 5% level (c.v. $= 5.991$): association

The cells with the largest values of $\dfrac{(f_o - f_e)^2}{f_e}$ are

medium/induction and long/induction so medium and long service seem to be associated, respectively, with more than and fewer than expected employees with induction-only training.

8 $X^2 = 2.527$

$v = 2$

Accept H_0 at 5% level (c.v. $= 5.991$): no association

9 (i) $X^2 = 5.36$

$v = 2$

Reject H_0 at 10% level (c.v. $= 4.605$): association

(ii) Two degrees of freedom, since once the urban/none and urban/one values are fixed, all the other cell values follow from the row and column totals.

(iii) It appears that fewer rural residents than expected read more than one newspaper.

10 $X^2 = 22.18$

$v = 9$

Reject H_0 at 5% level (c.v. $= 16.92$): association

Considering the values of $\dfrac{(f_o - f_e)^2}{f_e}$ for each cell,

shows that rural areas seem to be associated with more reasonable and excellent and less poor or good air quality than expected.

11 H_0: no association, H_1: association

$X^2 = 19.79$, c.v. $= 16.81$

Reject H_0, seems to be association

SE and Midlands have more short and fewer long lifespans than expected; 'rest' has fewer short and more long lifespans than expected.

Exercise 3C (Page 97)

1 (i) $H_0: \mu = 1000$, $H_1: \mu < 1000$

(ii) $z = 0.6$, which is not in the critical region for any of the usual significance levels.

(iii) $z = -1.63$, not significant

2 (i) $H_0: \mu = 1.73$, $H_1: \mu > 1.73$

(ii) $N(1.73, 0.0008)$

(iii)

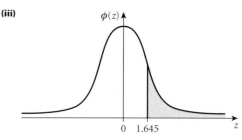

(iv) $z = 1.24$, not significant; You must assume that heights in the local area are representative of heights of men in general.

3 (i) 75

(ii) $H_0: \mu = 0$, $H_1: \mu \neq 0$

(iii) $z = 2.19$, significant

(iv) If σ^2 was larger, z would be smaller. If z became smaller than the critical value, 1.96, the opposite conclusion would be reached.

4 (i) $H_0: \mu = 1424$, $H_1: \mu > 1424$

(ii) $z = 1.70$, significant

5 (i) $H_0: \mu = 40.5$, $H_1: \mu < 40.5$

(ii) $z = -0.87$, not significant

6 (i) $H_0: \mu = 1.32$, $H_1: \mu \neq 1.32$

(ii) $z = -1.05$, not significant

7 (i) $H_0: \mu = 1930$, $H_1: \mu > 1930$

(ii) $z = 1.60$, not significant

8 (i) H_0: no association; H_1: association

$X^2 = 15.76$

$v = 6$

Reject H_0 at 2.5% level (c.v. $= 14.45$): association

(ii) The outstanding feature is that business members are much more interested in the social facilities than would have been expected if there were no association. The other main points of divergence are that business members are less interested in outdoor courts, while individual members are more interested in the gymnasium and less interested in the social facilities.

9 (i) H_0: no association; H_1: association

$X^2 = 12.406$

$v = 6$

Reject H_0 at 10% level (c.v. $= 10.64$): association

(ii) No single category makes a large contribution to the X^2 statistic but there are many smaller contributions from a number of categories: locals tend to be light spenders and not heavy, those travelling a medium distance tend to be medium spenders but not light and coach people tend to be medium spenders but not heavy.

10 (i) H_0: no association; H_1: association

(ii) $X^2 = 14.71$

$v = 6$

Reject H_0 at 5% level (c.v. $= 12.59$): association

(iii) The key feature is that people from 'other areas' bring far more old appliances than would be expected if there were no association.

(iv) In the absence of association the rows and columns are independent, therefore
$$P(\text{in cell } (i, j)) = P(\text{in row } i) \times P(\text{in row } j)$$
which can be estimated by $\dfrac{n_{i.}}{n} \times \dfrac{n_{.j}}{n}$.

The estimated frequency in cell (i, j) is
$$n \times \text{this} = \dfrac{n_{i.} \, n_{.j}}{n}.$$

11 (i) H_0: no association; H_1: association

(ii) $X^2 = 19.87$

$v = 6$

Reject H_0 at 5% level (c.v. $= 12.59$): association

(iii) There are very many fewer medium home-related payouts than expected – home-related payouts tend to be either high or low. There are many fewer low work-related payouts than expected – these tend to be high. Travel-related payouts have some tendency not to be high.

12 $X^2 = 2.3445$

$v = 1$

Accept H_0 at 5% level (c.v. $= 3.84$): independent

13 (i) H_0: no association; H_1: association

(ii) $X^2 = 11.2791$

$v = 2$

Reject H_0 at 1% level (c.v. $= 9.21$): association

(iii) The number of male teachers in higher education makes the greatest contribution. The proportion of male teachers increases as age group increases.

Chapter 4

❓ (Page 104)

See text that follows.

Exercise 4A (Page 116)

1 (i) -0.8

(ii) 0

(iii) 0.8

2 (i) (a)

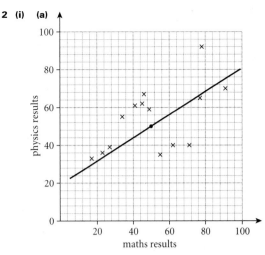

There appears to be positive linear correlation.

(b) 0.560; This confirms there is positive linear correlation.

(ii) (a)

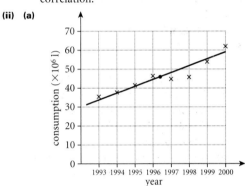

There appears to be strong positive linear correlation.

(b) 0.940; This confirms there is strong positive linear correlation.

(iii) (a)

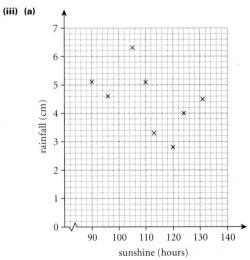

There appears to be no linear correlation (or very weak negative linear correlation).

(b) −0.461; This confirms there is weak negative linear correlation.

(iv) (a)

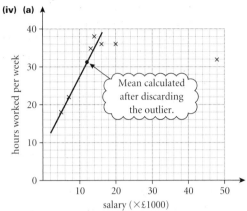

There appears to be positive linear correlation, if the outlier is discarded.

(b) 0.895 (after discarding the outlier); This confirms there is positive linear correlation.

(v) (a)

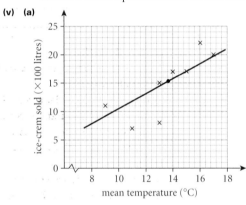

There appears to be positive linear correlation.

(b) 0.802; This confirms there is positive linear correlation.

(vi) (a)

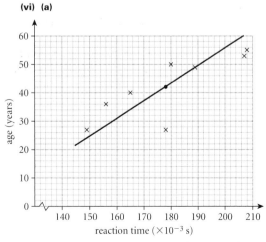

There appears to be positive linear correlation.

(b) 0.806; This confirms there is positive linear correlation.

3 (i) 0.704

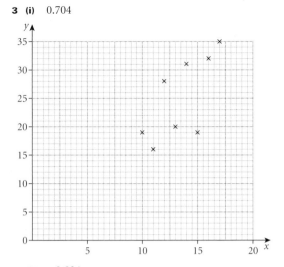

(ii) −0.924

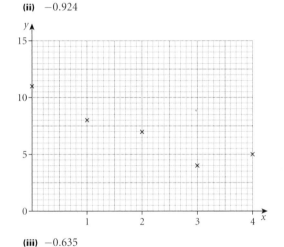

(iii) −0.635

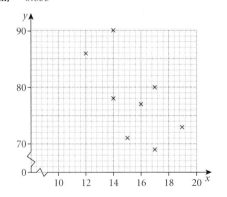

(iv) -0.128

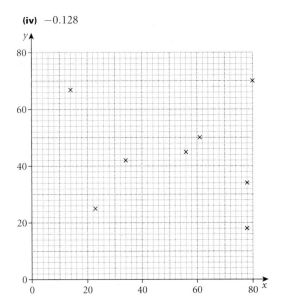

Exercise 4B (Page 125)

1 (i) 0.913
  (ii) $H_0: \rho = 0$, $H_1: \rho > 0$
  (iii) Accept H_1

2 (i) 0.380
  (ii) $H_0: \rho = 0$ (Jamila), $H_1: \rho > 0$ (coach)
  (iii) Accept H_0; there is not enough evidence to reject H_0. r needs to be > 0.4973 to reject H_0 at the 5% significance level.

3 (i) 0.715
  (ii) $H_0: \rho = 0$, $H_1: \rho > 0$
  (iii) Accept H_1; it seems that performance in high jump and long jump have positive correlation.

4 (i) 0.850
  (ii) $H_0: \rho = 0$, $H_1: \rho > 0$
  (iii) Accept H_1; Yes

5 (i) 0.946
  (ii) $H_0: \rho = 0$, $H_1: \rho > 0$
  (iii) Accept H_1; there is very strong positive correlation.

6 $H_0: \rho = 0$, $H_1: \rho > 0$; $r = 0.901$; Andrew

7 (i) $H_0: \rho = 0$, $H_1: \rho \neq 0$, 5% sig. level
  (ii) 0.491, accept H_1
  (iii)

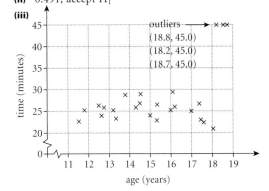

Outliers: (18.8, 45), (18.2, 45), (18.7, 45), it seems as though these girls stopped for a rest.

(iv) The scatter diagram should have been drawn first and the outliers investigated before calculating the product moment correlation coefficient. With the three outliers removed, $r = -0.1612$, accept H_0.

8 (i) 0.807
  (ii) $H_0: \rho = 0$, $H_1: \rho > 0$
  (iii) Accept H_1
  (iv)

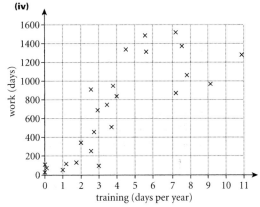

  (v) Giving more training to employees does tend to keep staff with the company.

9 (i) $H_0: \rho = 0$, $H_1: \rho < 0$; $r = -0.854$, accept H_1
  (ii) Correlation does not imply causation. Perhaps Charlotte ought to gather some data herself to highlight the hazards of drinking alcohol, e.g. wine consumption/liver disease.

10 $r = 0.59$. Diagram suggests moderate positive correlation which is confirmed by the fairly high positive value of r.
  After eliminating the high and low values, $r = -0.145$. Discarding high and low values of x seems to produce an uncorrelated set.

11 (i) 0.3377
  (ii) $H_0: \rho = 0$, $H_1: \rho > 0$; $0.3377 < 0.5214$ so accept H_0.
  (iii) It reduces the value of the product moment correlation coefficient. It should be included, unless there is any reason to suppose it is an error, as it is as valid as any other point.

12 (i)

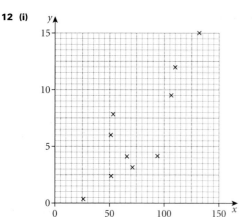

(ii) 0.834

(iii) $H_0: \rho = 0, H_1: \rho > 0$; critical values: 0.5494 (5%), 0.7155 (1%); $0.834 > 0.7155$ so reject H_0.

(iv) The student's view is wrong; correlation does not imply causation. In this case a common underlying cause, such as wealth, seems plausible.

Exercise 4C (Page 137)

1 0.576

2 −0.0875; Use test C and possibly one other test.

3 (i) Y and Z

(ii) $H_0: \rho = 0, H_1: \rho > 0$, accept H_1 at 5% significance level.

4 (i) 0.766, −0.143

(ii) $H_0: \rho = 0, H_1: \rho > 0$, accept H_1.

(iii) Product moment correlation coefficient is more suitable here because it takes into account the magnitude of the variables.

5 (i) 0.636. Positive sign indicates possible positive correlation.

(ii) $H_0: \rho = 0, H_1: \rho \neq 0$, accept H_1; There is some association between time taken and quality of work.

6 (i) 0.680

(ii) $H_0: \rho = 0, H_1: \rho > 0$, $0.680 > 0.6694$ so accept H_1.

(iii) 0.214

(iv) The two correlation coefficients measure different quantities. The product moment correlation coefficient measures linear correlation using the actual data values. Spearman's coefficient measures rank correlation using the data ranks. Mr Smith ought to have used Spearman's coefficient.

7 (i) 0.636

(ii) $H_0: \rho = 0, H_1: \rho > 0$, accept H_0

(iii) It is more appropriate to use the product

moment correlation coefficent since it utilises the actual data values.

8 (i) 0.881

(ii) 0.888

(iii) 0.622

There is significant correlation at the 5% level in all three cases. There are outliers in **(i)** contraceptives, **(ii)** contraceptives and **(iii)** nuclear power.

9 (i) −0.7857

(ii) $H_0: \rho = 0, H_1: \rho \neq 0$; $-0.7857 < -0.7381$ so reject H_0

10 (i)

Rank for additive	Rank for weight
3	8
8	6
2	2
10	10
9	4
1	1
4	3
5	5
6	9
7	7

0.612

(ii) $H_0: \rho = 0, H_1: \rho > 0$; the alternative hypothesis is one-sided because the additive is claimed to enhance growth.

(iii) $0.612 > 0.5636$ so reject H_0.

(iv) This does not change the rankings so does not affect the conclusions.

11 (i) 0.1608

(ii) $H_0: \rho = 0, H_1: \rho > 0$; $0.5035 > 0.1608$ so accept H_0.

(iii) If $r_s = 0.15$ for the whole population then there is an association but it is weak.

12 (i) $r_s = 0.952$; $H_0: \rho = 0, H_1: \rho > 0$; $0.952 > 0.4637$ so reject H_0.

(ii) It is not justified; a strong association exists but this does not imply that poverty causes a higher death rate.

(iii) Death rates depend on age distributions, for example, an area with many old people will have a high death rate.

Exercise 4D (Page 148)

1 $19x + 50y = 1615$, 27.7

2 $1.446x + y = 114.38$, 53.7

3 (i), (ii), (iv)

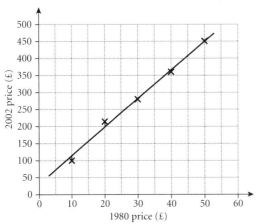

(ii) $y = 8.45x + 27.5$

(iii) This is roughly in line with the rest of the data. It is below the line, so the price increase is slightly below average.

(iv) -12, 18.5, -1, -5.5, 0

(v) 517.5; The least squares regression line gives the minimum value of the sum of the squares of the residuals. Altering the line would increase the sum.

4 (i)

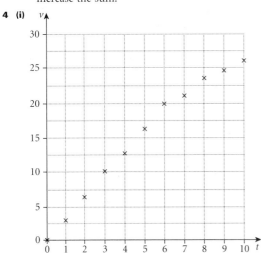

(ii) $v = 2.68t + 1.54$

(iii) 0.988

(iv) Modelling data by a single straight line assumes that the correlation is linear. However, looking at the scatter diagram there is a possibility that r is proportional to a power of t thus making the correlation non-linear.

5 (i), (ii)

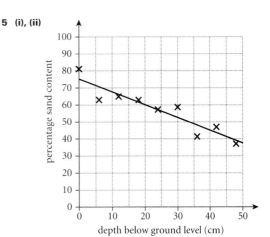

(ii) $y = -0.752x + 75.0$

(iii) When $x = 50$, $y = 37.4$; this is slightly outside the range of data values and so may not be reliable. When $x = 100$, $y = -0.2$; this is further outside the range of data values and there is no evidence that the linear correlation can be extrapolated.

(iv) 5.63, -7.46, -1.65, 1.06, 0.567, 6.78, -7.11, 3.50, -1.29;

$$\sum_{r=1}^{n}\left(y_r - \left(\bar{y} + \frac{S_{xy}}{S_{xx}}(x - \bar{x})\right)\right)$$
$$= \sum_{r=1}^{n} y_r - n\bar{y} - \frac{S_{xy}}{S_{xx}}\left(\sum_{r=1}^{n} x_r - n\bar{x}\right) = 0$$

6 (i)

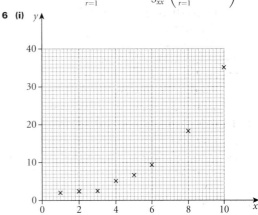

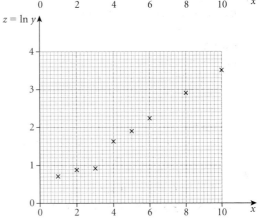

(ii) The line of regression of y on x is not very accurate because the correlation is not linear. The line of regression of z on x is much more accurate.

(iii) 12.8

7 (i)

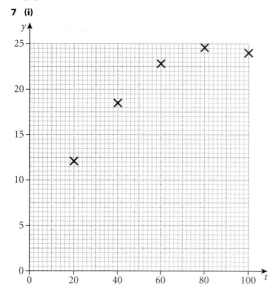

(ii) $y = 0.1495t + 11.43$

(iii) When $t = 30$, $y = 15.915$; likely to be accurate. When $t = 160$, $y = 35.35$; extrapolation very unlikely to be accurate.

(iv) The regression line does not provide a good model; the data appear to be distinctly non-linear. Perhaps there is a curved relationship or perhaps a levelling off in y.

8 (i)

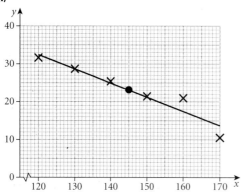

A straight line seems good for x at the low end of the range, but is suspect at the high end of the range.

(ii) $y = 77.289 - 0.374x$

(iii) When $x = 145$, $y = 23.06$; likely to be accurate as it is within the range of the data. When $x = 180$, $y = 9.97$; may not be accurate as it is beyond the range of the data.

(iv) The residuals represent the variation not explained by the regression line; the square of the residuals is minimised by the least squares regression line.

9 (i)

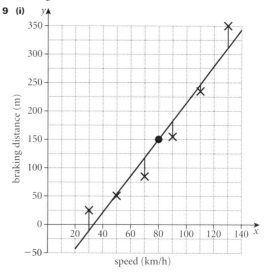

(ii) $y = 3.214x - 107.1$

(iii) When $x = 100$, $y = 214$; seems reasonable since it is within the data range and fits with the neighbouring points. When $x = 150$, $y = 375$; probably unreliable since the value $x = 150$ lies outside the data range and there is no indication that the linear relationship can be extrapolated.

(iv) The regression line does not seem to provide a good model; a curve may fit the data better.

10 Regression line of y on x: $y = 0.78x + 24.0$ or approx. $y = x + \frac{1}{4}(100 - x)$, thus $\approx \frac{1}{4}$.

Exercise 4E (page 151)

1 (i) 0.473

(ii) $H_0: \rho = 0$, $H_1: \rho > 0$, c.v. = 0.3783; since $0.473 > 0.3783$, reject H_0. There is just sufficient evidence to conclude that there is a positive correlation between heights and masses. The scatter diagram is elliptical, implying that the sample could be taken from a bivariate Normal population.

(iii) Being tall does not necessarily imply that one is heavy; positive correlation is weak and the scatter diagram shows many cases where a reduction in height is associated with an increase in mass, and vice versa.

2 (i) $H_0: \rho = 0$, $H_1: \rho \neq 0$; 2-tail test is used because the analyst does not specify a positive or a negative correlation.

(ii)

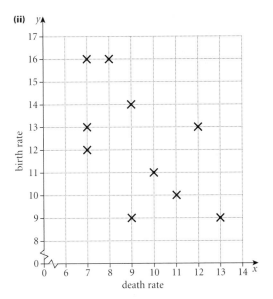

birth rate (y-axis), death rate (x-axis)

(iii) -0.574

(iv) Since $-0.574 > -0.6319$, accept H_0; the death rates and birth rates are not correlated.

(v) There is weak negative correlation between death rates and birth rates.

(vi) No, the additional evidence shows that H_0 should be rejected.

3 (i) -0.44 (2 s.f.)

(ii) $H_0: \rho = 0$, $H_1: \rho < 0$; c.v. $= -0.3961 > -0.44$, so reject H_0.

(iii) The sample is not representative in time or space.

(iv) The distribution must be bivariate Normal, which seems reasonable in this case.

4 (i) $H_0: \rho = 0$, $H_1: \rho \neq 0$

(ii) $r = 0.661$ (3 s.f.), c.v. $= 0.5614$, reject H_0; the population must be bivariate Normal

(iii) $\Sigma x = 708$, $\Sigma y = 1001$, $\Sigma x^2 = 25\,362$, $\Sigma y^2 = 50\,459$, $n = 20$, $\Sigma xy = 35\,212.5$

(iv) The incorrect pair produce an extreme point to the right and below the cluster thereby producing negative correlation.

5 (i) $\frac{2}{3}$

(ii) $H_0: \rho = 0$, $H_1: \rho > 0$, c.v. $= 0.5636$, reject H_0 implying the judges are in broad agreement

(iii) c.v. $= 0.5494$, reject H_0 implying the judges are in broad agreement

(iv) The rank correlation hypothesis test is more appropriate since the data gives rank order and the sample is unlikely to come from a bivariate Normal population.

6 (i)

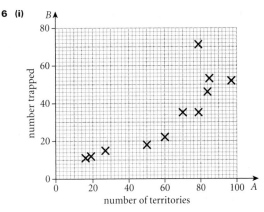

number trapped (y-axis), number of territories (x-axis)

(ii) 0.916 (3 s.f.)

(iii) $H_0: \rho = 0$, $H_1: \rho \neq 0$, c.v. $= 0.6182$, $0.916 > 0.6182$ so reject H_0, generally, the greater the number of territories recorded, the greater the number trapped.

(iv) It would be less appropriate; the data do not seem to conform to a linear pattern and there is no real evidence of an elliptical scatter.

7 (i)

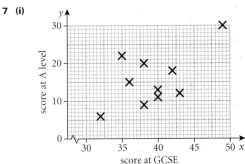

score at A level (y-axis), score at GCSE (x-axis)

(ii) 0.291

(iii) $H_0: \rho = 0$, $H_1: \rho > 0$

(iv) $0.5636 > 0.291$ so accept H_0

(v) $0.5494 < 0.5807$ so reject H_0; the product moment correlation coefficient has been affected by the extreme value, $(49, 30)$.

(vi) The product moment correlation coefficient is influenced by extreme values but Spearman's coefficient of rank correlation is not; the sample is small and not sufficient to demonstrate a bivariate Normal distribution, so it is doubtful that the product moment correlation coefficient is appropriate.

8 (i)

Team	Rank for position	Rank for attendance
Barnsley	8	6
Birmingham	3	2
Bolton	2	5
Burnley	6	4
Grimsby	11	11
Portsmouth	10	8
Preston	5	7
Sheffield Utd	7	9
Watford	1	1
W. Bromwich	4	3
Wimbledon	9	10

$r_s = 0.85$ (2 s.f.)

$H_0: \rho = 0$, $H_1: \rho > 0$, c.v. $= 0.7091$,

$0.85 > 0.7091$ so reject H_0, and conclude that there is a positive association between league position and attendance at the next match.

(ii) The modelling assumption is that the sample is taken at random from the population. In this case the sample is not really random, just a random Saturday, however, it could be representative of the season.

(iii) A higher position might not cause a higher attendance; there will be other factors such as the population density of the surrounding area and counter-attractions.

9 (i)

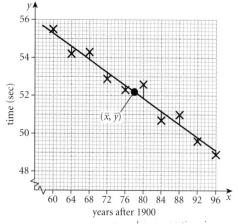

years after 1900

(ii) $y = 65.72 - 0.1733x$

(iii) See graph

(iv) When $x = 100$, $y = 48.39$; this is slightly outside the range of data values and so may not be reliable.

When $x = 120$, $y = 44.92$; this is further outside the range of data values and there is no evidence that the linear correlation can be extrapolated.

(v) The equation of the regression line is found by minimising the sum of the squares of the residuals.

10 (i)

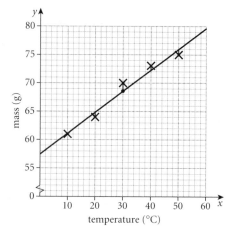

(ii) $y = 0.37x + 57.5$

(iii) 70.45 g; 0 °C to 60 °C; unwise to extrapolate outside the data set.

(iv) $-0.2, -0.9, 1.4, 0.7, -1.0$

(v) The equation of the regression line is found by minimising the sum of the squares of the residuals.

11 (i)

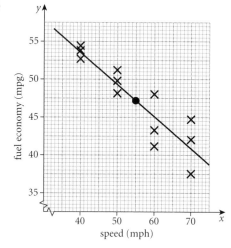

(ii) $y = 70.527 - 0.424x$

(iii) (a) 51.45 mpg

(b) 43.0 mpg

(iv) The prediction for 45 mph is more reliable than that for 65 mph, since the regression line is a better fit at lower speeds; as the speeds increase, the values for the fuel economy have a wider spread and so the use of the regression line to make predictions, especially at the upper end, is dubious.

12 (i) $y = 86.77 - 6.35x$

When $x = 4.3$, $y = 59.4$; fairly inaccurate since, although it is within the range of the data, the fit does not look good.

When $x = 15$, $y = -8.5$; unsatisfactory since not only is it outside the range of the data but it also implies that the coffee will freeze.

(ii)

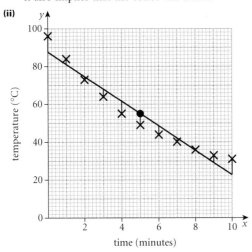

Since the residuals are first negative, then positive and finally negative, a linear regression line does not seem to be appropriate; a curve may be a better fit.

Index